Copper, Timber, Iron and Heart

Stories from Michigan's Upper Peninsula

Books also written by Ben Mukkala

Tour Guide: Big Bay and Huron Mountains

Come On Along: Tales & Trails of the North Woods

Copper, Timber, Iron and Heart: Stories from Michigan's Upper Peninsula

Photo credits for cover pictures are shared by:
The author
Superior View Studios, Marquette, MI
Mr. Jack Anderson

Copper, Timber, Iron and Heart

Stories from Michigan's Upper Peninsula

by

Ben Mukkala

Still Waters Publishing
Marquette Michigan
2003

Copper, Timber, Iron and Heart

All photography in this book is the work of the author
except where indicated otherwise.

Published by Still Waters Publishing, 2003

Limited first edition 2,000 copies May 2003

ISBN 0-9709971-2-4

"If a man takes no thought about what is distant, he will find sorrow near at hand."

Confucius (551 – 479 B.C.)

Dedication

"... The purpose of life is to *matter* – to count, to stand for something, to have it make some difference that we have lived at all."

Leo C. Rosten

This book is respectfully dedicated to

You,

The Reader

If these pages inform you, if you enjoy them, if they give a little insight, warm your heart, if they lighten your burdens even just for a day, then I have "made some difference," I have "mattered."

Acknowledgements

This page is to acknowledge the help received from others. It's in recognition of those I couldn't have done without - and a plea for forgiveness to those I have disappointed. I don't guess it interests you who read the book but it fulfills an obligation and confesses personal shortcomings.

In appreciation I should include all those who taught me about life and living, the standards and ethics by which I believe a "good" person should abide. A fella's mother and father immediately come to mind - and the memory of a Grandfather who coughed his life away after working for years in the copper mines. Then too there were a couple of wars along the way. There's nothing like the impersonal terror of war-up-close to tear the tinsel from the fundamentals of life.

For the immediate task I must thank my wife, Dorothy, for her never failing encouragement, Ms. Stacey Willey who never hesitated to tell me if I was about to screw something up and those kind folks who read and commented on my work – Thank You. Responsibility for mistakes of course is mine.

Last but not least I wish to thank you folks who choose to read these pages. Without you there's no need for any of it.

Enjoy! I hope I don't disappoint you.

Table of Contents

Sailors & Lifesavers 5

The Loggers 31

Introduction 31
The Trees 33
The "Shanty Boys" 41
The River Hogs 56
The Walkin' Boss 67
The Prayer 79

The Hired Hand 81

The Iron Miners 87

Finding the Ore 87
The Early Years 93
"Noblesse Oblige" 102
Disaster! 110
A Miner's Miner 120
Here and Now 125

Fishermen - & Women 131

The Copper Miners 139

Prologue 139

The Survivor 141

In the Beginning 141
Minong 145
The Lure of Copper 147
The Exploration 157
Regroup 162
Supplies 165
The Plan 172

The Investment 173
The Dream 175
Preparation 177
The Investors 179
Dig In 182
Mission Accomplished 183
Shelter 184
The Shares 186
Food 188
The Lawyer 191
Madness 193
The Return 197
Alone 207
Return Home 212
The Treatment 218
and so it goes 219

EDUCATORS 221

THE KEWEENAW 227

Discovery 227
The Mines 231
The People 237
The Italian Hall Disaster 246
The End of Copper 249

WHERE DREAMS COME TRUE 253

TO ORDER BOOKS 263

AUTHORS BIOGRAPHY 265

PHOTOGRAPHS

Lifesavers 5

White Pine 33

Camp Breakfast 41

Hazardous Work 55

Lake Independence Lumber Co. 67

Chapel in the Forest 78

The Farmer 81

Iron Ore Stump 87

Jackson Mine 93

William G. Mather 101

Barnes Hecker Monument 109

Ernie Ronn 119

Time to Celebrate 125

The "Peter A" *131*

Isle Royale *141*

Cora and Fred Jeffers *221*

Keweenaw Peninsula *227*

Quincy Mine *231*

Calumet *237*

Italian Hall Memorial *245*

Once a Miner's Home *249*

Bay Cliff's Children *253*

Ben Mukkala *265*

Front Cover Index *266*

Rear Cover Index *267*

Photo from Superior View Studio, Marquette, MI

Lifesavers

The Marquette Station's Life Saving Crew poses in the station's life boat. The smaller surf boat is shown in the foreground.

SAILORS & LIFESAVERS

Lake Superior, the greatest of the Great Lakes, is often referred to as "The Great Inland Sea." There is an adage that states that "the sea is terribly unforgiving of any incapacity or neglect." Few who go down to this sea in ships will argue that point.

The great lakes were and are an important feature in the development of our north country. First traversed by the "Voyageurs" in canoes the expansion of the area's resources demanded more and more of the great waters. The development of the Locks enabling ships to be raised and lowered around the St. Mary's River rapids at Sault Ste. Marie, the "Soo," truly opened up Lake Superior to water commerce.

Early sailors were taught the many moods of the Great Lakes by trial and error. The unfortunate feature of such education is that experience first administers the test and then teaches the lesson. Some never made it past the test stage. Their bones litter the seabed.

This is a tale-to-be-told concerning the caliber of those ". . .who went down to the sea in ships, who did business on great waters."

It began as a beautiful day in September, 1895, in Upper Michigan's north country. The "Charles J. "Kershaw," a 1300 ton steam powered wooden tug, was up-bound on Lake Superior with two schooners in tow, the "Moonlight" and the "Kent." Fall was in air but Indian summer was on the gentle south wind that barely rippled the calm surface of the big lake.

The coming of steam engines to power ships enabled Captains to more efficiently meet schedules. Ships dependent on sail were at the mercy of the vagaries of wind and weather in determining times of arrival and departure. Many old sailing ships were now being utilized as barges towed behind steam-powered vessels

In the engine room of the "Kershaw" the grizzled Chief Engineer stood staring at the engine's main steam feed line. He had discovered a hairline crack in a high-pressure line during a routine inspection. The "Kershaw" was some twenty years old and beginning show evidence of wear and tear after these many years plying the great lakes.

He had brought the condition to the attention of the Captain before leaving port at the Soo. All things considered the two men decided to continue in spite of the condition. With winter fast approaching the supplies aboard the "Kershaw" and the two schooners were critical to the village of Marquette.

The weather was beautiful. The Chief recommended wrapping the steam pipe tightly with chain to support the weakened pipe. Along with the chain they agreed to lower the steam pressure. It would reduce the power output of the engines but that was an acceptable condition. The shipping season was drawing to a close and the ship would soon be docked for a general refit.

As he gazed at the chain-wrapped pipe leakage in the area of the fracture appeared to be minimal. He removed the cigar stub from between his teeth, grunted to himself and moved on.

The 14-man crew of the "Kershaw" had been sailing together for several seasons and the operation of the ship ran as smoothly as a well-oiled clock. There were two new men aboard, one on the deck and the other as cook's helper. The Captain was widely respected and duty aboard the "Kershaw" was looked upon as choice. Men competed to fill any crew vacancy that might occur. The new men seemed to fit in well.

The Captain was a seasoned Great Lake's sailor, knowledgeable about the lakes and their peculiarities, and showed concern for the welfare of his crew. Everyone was confident in his ability to handle the ship. The two schooners in tow, the "Moonlight" and the "Kent," trailed the "Kershaw" amicably on their tethers.

With the Whitefish Point Light safely astern and the Grand Island Light anticipated soon all seemed to be progressing nicely. The Chief had adjusted the over-pressure valve on the boiler to insure reduced pressure. He also admonished the coal passers to ease off on feeding the fire. The engine churned contentedly in its bed. Oilers made their rounds lubricating the valve followers and the connecting rods. The Chief did, occasionally, lean over the engine guardrail to stare into the dimly lit main line passageway for evidence of any further weakening of the pressure line.

The Chief's concern was unconsciously exhibited by his nervous worrying of his cigar stub. The chewing had frayed the stub rather badly. The engine room crew, attuned to the moods of their Chief, recognized the signs and exchanged knowing glances. Everybody had better stay on their toes.

With the Grand Island Light close on the port bow the wind began to shift. Almost imperceptibly at first it swung from the south to the southeast to the east. It began to increase. Clouds were visible to the northwest as the sun was sliding down the western horizon. In the wheelhouse a furrow had begun to crease the Captain's brow. He instructed the helmsman to steer further north, away from Grand Island as a precaution to the shifting wind. Far ahead a bolt of lightning flashed briefly followed several moments later by the muffled rumble of thunder. The Captain strode to the wheelhouse window, leaned against the coaming and stared hard at the horizon ahead.

Marquette harbor was partially protected by a breakwater and provided a secure anchorage. There were many who felt that all rocks and shoals in the harbor had not yet been charted. The Captain's concern was that, with the two schooners in tow, he would need additional maneuvering room, especially if the weather made up. Glancing astern he noted the waves making up with foam from the occasional breaking wave grinning back, white against the gathering darkness.

The "Moonlight" and the "Kent" began to respond to the shifting building wind by swinging to port. He congratulated himself for foreseeing this possibility and pulling clear of Grand Island.

Down in the engine room the "black gang" was relieved by the next shift otherwise all remained unchanged. The Chief instructed the incoming crew on the care and feeding of the boiler then left the engine room for the mess deck and dinner.

Arriving at the officer's table in the dining area he was surprised not to see the Captain. It was not a scheduled thing but the routine aboard ship had become so fixed that the Chief Engineer and the Captain usually found themselves at meals together. Thinking the Captain would come in momentarily the Chief sat down and proceeded with his meal.

As time passed and the Captain didn't appear a faint expression of concern creased the Chief's features. He continued eating but resolved to go forward to the wheelhouse if the Captain did not make an appearance. The deck vibrated contentedly beneath his feet assuring the Chief that all was well in the engine room. The vessel drove steadily onward. An occasional light jolt indicated that the towed vessels were becoming a bit restless. Leaning over to peer astern he, too, noted the wind shift and wave action building from the east-northeast.

Up in the wheelhouse the helmsman was relieved. The Captain ordered a slight northward shift in heading to further compensate for the shifting wind. Ahead, against the darkening horizon, the play of lightning was even more apparent. The occasional grumble of thunder was still muted and distant.

The wheelhouse door suddenly opened and the Chief entered. Shaking a little spray from his cap and jacket he greeted the Captain. "How's it lookin'?"

The Captain glanced toward the Chief and shook his head slightly. The Chief glanced at the helmsman who stoically monitored the binnacle, moving the wheel a spoke or two and seemed not to notice the conversation. The Chief had expected a reassuring and jovial response from the Captain but his glance relayed concern for the situation. The Captain was a steady hand and took pains not to alarm members of the crew. He and the Chief Engineer however had a special relationship developed over many years at sea together.

Command is a lonely calling and fortunate is the commander who has someone to whom he can turn. The Captain and the Chief enjoyed such a relationship. Glancing once more at the darkening western horizon the Captain, with a slight jerk of his head indicated to the Chief they should confer in his sea cabin directly behind the wheelhouse. The two men filed out of the wheelhouse.

"She's makin' up ahead, Chief. We're still about four and a half or five hours out of Marquette. Lightning is dancing all along the western horizon. I might need more power from those engines."

The Chief nodded his understanding. "I felt the tow jerking at her halter a bit. What's the situation there?"

"Well, we can't very well abandon them to sail with a nor'easter makin' up and darkness comin' on. The towing tackle is stout enough to hold. The problem is going to be one of power."

The Chief shook his head in understanding. "I've got 'er chained down tight and the pressure relief valve backed off. That crack shows no sign of having gotten any worse. I can try to tighten the chain a bit more and stand by to increase the pressure. Don't call for more power unless you really need it. If the main line blows," he shook his head again, "we're dead in the water."

The Captain gripped the Chief's shoulder briefly. The two men looked at each other. "Maybe it won't happen, Chief. Maybe I'm borrowing trouble but, if it comes, we'd better be ready for it." He grinned and shrugged, then looked into the other man's eyes. "Chief, I understand the situation in the engine room but if I have to call for power, give me all you've got."

The Chief returned the Captain's grim look, nodded and replied, "If you call for it, I'll give you the best I can deliver."

"I can't ask for better than that. Let's hope we have good luck."

As the Chief moved aft the jerking of the ships in tow had become decidedly more pronounced. Some of the following waves were now breaking over the starboard quarter and drenched him. No matter. The engine room would be warm. Before this night was over it might be much warmer still.

The crews aboard the towed vessels had recognized the change in the weather. There were limited means of communication between the ships but it was apparent that the "Kershaw" was already involved in compensating for the changes. The crews aboard the "Moonlight" and the "Kent" scurried about securing their ships in case the situation worsened. There was nothing more they could do but steer their course docilely behind the "Kershaw."

At Marquette lightning and thunder ruled the skies. A gusty wind was blowing and rain had begun to fall. The lighthouse beacon flashed its identifying code bravely into the encroaching darkness. Downstairs the men of the lifesaving station idly played cards, read, or prepared for bed.

Darkness came earlier with each passing day. Winter was approaching and off-time diversions were few. The crew tending the light had returned and was hanging their wet weather gear near the wood stove to dry. Someone made a comment to the cook about the night's dinner and was answered with a sudden scowl.

"No! No! It was good! I like my stew with a little sand in it. It's good for the digestion."

"I'll give you 'digestion.' I'll . . ."

The station chief broke in, "Now, now, children. Mustn't play rough games in the living room. John," turning to the complainer, "if you're not satisfied with cookies chow, get your butt out into the kitchen and wash the sand from those dirty plates."

The cook grinned good-naturedly. John's head jerked his head up in surprise only to be greeted by laughter from the entire crew. He and John laughed in response and John retorted, "Come on, cookie, I'll give you a hand out there."

The lifesaver crew was a smooth functioning group whose lives often depended upon one another. They were a well-matched and smooth running operation. They were good at what they did – and they knew it. They joked with one another frequently and it was rare that anyone took offense. Laughter and good humor went a long way to relieve the boredom that accompanied their job.

They worked hard at maintaining their seamanship skills and their physical condition. Their time was spent waiting for their fellow man to get into trouble. When they were called upon they had to have the answers immediately. Each man knew his job, his partner's job, and they were able to interchange immediately. The crew at Marquette had a reputation and the awards that went with it for excellence in lifesaving.

The "Moonlight" and the "Kent" were responding to the building seas by continually jerking against their tow and each other. The ride for both crews was growing more and more uneasy with the passage of time.

The Chief Engineer aboard the "Kershaw" sent two of his crew up into the steam pipe passage to tighten the chain, if they could around the weakened pipe. The ship was beginning to pitch in the following sea and the towed vessels jerking in an irregular fashion weren't helping their efforts. After thirty minutes or so the men climbed down, drenched with sweat and wiping their hands. They stated that it didn't appear the pressure line was bleeding much steam. As far as the tightening was concerned, well, with a shake of the head, they'd done the best they could. The Chief nodded, patted one of the men on the back and thanked them both for their efforts.

Up in the wheelhouse the "Kershaw" was almost beam on to the wind and waves. She was gaining forward motion from the weather while using what power it had to claw away from the shoreline. The Captain had been on the bridge for the past six hours continuously. The cook had sent him a sandwich and some hot coffee. It sat beside the coaming where the messenger had placed it, untouched.

The problem had become one of geometry, of angles and vectors. The force of the gale – and it had made up into a gale – and the following waves were forcing the vessels toward the unfriendly shore. The Captain, by turning further and further into the wind, was attempting to offset the force pressing him south while allowing the westward vector of the wind and weather to carry him to the lee of Marquette's breakwater. Once in the shelter of the breakwater his reduced power would be sufficient to reach a safe anchorage for himself and his charges. The problem was that the sea was overcoming available engine power. It was becoming apparent that without more power the battle would be lost. Reluctantly he called a seaman to his side and sent him to the engine room with a simple but grave request: "Chief, I need that power."

The Chief Engineer looked into the face of the young messenger. He was one of the new men and it was evident that he sensed the gravity of the situation. His face was pale in the subdued light.

"You're sure the Captain said 'that power,' not 'just a little more power?'"

The boy shook his head enthusiastically. "No, Chief, he definitely said 'that power,' like you'd know what he meant."

"I'm afraid I do," the Chief replied. Then, noticing the near panic in the lad's eyes, the Chief managed to smile reassuringly. He shook the boys shoulder and said, "You'll remember this night, lad. It'll be a story to tell your grandchildren."

He turned to his crew, motioned to the coalbunkers and said, "Pour it on, men. The Captain needs the power."

The firebox door was opened and shovel after shovel of coal was flung in. The Chief reluctantly tightened the relief valve and stood looking at the chain wrapped steam line. The cadence of the engines gradually increased. The vibration of the deck plates took on a more serious, frantic trembling.

Engine vibration is the nervous system of any ship. Men who follow the sea sense the changing tensions aboard ship even in their sleep. There was not a man aboard who didn't sense the change, who didn't realize that the "Kershaw," the "Moonlight" and the "Kent" were in a struggle with the impersonal power of the sea.

At the Marquette Lifesaving Station a crewman was on watch in the tower. He scanned the sea from one obscured beach across what he could see of the rolling crashing water to the opposite beach area. He wondered what poor soul might be unlucky enough to be out there on a night like this.

From the corner of his eye he thought he caught a glimpse of a light – a red light. He looked back. Nothing! He raised his binoculars and peered in the direction from which he thought he saw the light. Binoculars, in addition to magnification, gather available light and improve a person's ability to see in darkness. He guessed it was just - No! Wait! There it was again! And there also appeared to be a white masthead light waving wildly back and forth.

Why a red light? If it was a ship southeast of the station a red light would mean he was seeing the port side of the vessel. That ship appeared to be heading out to sea. Why? Well, he'd wonder about that later. Right now he felt he should get down to the station and tell them there was a ship out there in the storm.

Aboard the "Kershaw" the Captain thought he could make out the Marquette Light – and the light at the end of the breakwater. It was going to be a near thing. He estimated that he still had about three miles to go, about thirty minutes under present conditions. Just then large wave struck broadside and simultaneously the "Kent" jerked at the towline. The shock almost knocked the Captain off his feet. The helmsman was knocked to his knees and the wheel spun downwind. The bow fell off to port before the helmsman could regain control and the ship, responding to the sudden deviation struggled to regain position in the merciless waves.

The Captain took the wheel and sent the helmsman hurrying to the engine room with a desperate request. "More power!" "Tell the Chief what's happening up here and tell him we need it all!"

When the helmsman reached the engine room he found the Chief braced against a stanchion while the men desperately struggled to maintain their balance and shovel coal into the fire. The Chief sent the helmsman back to the wheelhouse with his reply. "We're doin' the best that we can. Good luck!"

Halfway back to the wheelhouse the helmsman felt the deck heave upward beneath his feet accompanied by a deafening roar.

In the engine room scalding steam filled the steam line passageway. Bits of chain and fractured pieces of steam pipe had exploded like shrapnel. The straining pistons and connecting rods stopped dead.

A quick check of the black gang found that miraculously no one had been seriously injured. Evaluating the situation the Chief Engineer instructed the men to go topside. "There's nothing more we can do here and we'll have to cut the schooners loose."

"But – what'll they do if we cut them loose?"

The Chief looked briefly at the questioner and replied, "The same thing we're going to do – pray!"

On deck the crew had released the towline and the "Moonlight" and the "Kent" rapidly disappeared from view.

The Captain had broken out the emergency flares and, hanging tightly to the railing, fired a flare up and in the direction of the Marquette Light.

Ashore the first question the stationmaster asked was, "Was there a distress signal? Is the ship in trouble?"

"No distress signal but, if they're out there tonight, I'd say they're in trouble"

Both men returned to the lookout tower. The Station Master and the lookout had just reached the tower. The lookout cried out, pointing. A bright red flare arced high in the air and curved back into the sea. The Station Master didn't pause. "Keep watch and record whatever you see. We're on our way."

He hurried below and roused the crew, those who weren't still up, and quickly briefed them on the situation. "There's a ship in trouble to the southeast. We'll probably have to go by land to the beach downwind of them and work from there. We'll take the surfboat. The lifeboat is too large and heavy. It'd slow us down. Get the horses hitched up and load the boat on the wagon. Move! I'll go back to the tower and get a better fix on its location, try to ascertain its position. Maybe they'll fetch up on the sandy beach."

There was no need for further discussion. Each man knew his job. They had trained and practiced these drills. This time it was not practice.

Back aboard the "Kershaw" the Captain had assigned the flare pistol and flares to one of the seaman with instructions to fire one flare every three minutes.

The Chief Engineer struggled forward along the pitching deck. He fought his way up the ladder to the wheelhouse. The Captain was bent over examining a chart when he arrived.

"She's gone, Captain. I'm sorry but we did the best we could. The line just blew apart, chain and all. It didn't breech the hull anywhere I could see though"

"Don't blame yourself, Chief. I figured that's what happened. It looks like we're in God's hands now."

"How about the anchor? Any chance that . . ."

"I've got the men releasing the anchor but," he shrugged, "in this weather and being this close ashore, I don't give it much chance. It'll keep 'em busy though 'til we can come up with something else."

"How close ashore are we?"

Swinging an arm toward Marquette Light he replied, "That's Marquette Light right there. We were within minutes of making it in, Chief."

The Captain continued scanning the chart while the Chief gazed at Marquette Light whenever it came in view. "Captain, isn't the beach sand in this area? Maybe we'll fetch up on the shore?"

"That'd be a stroke of luck and we sure need a bit of that just now. I was just checking to see where we might . . ."

There was a tremendous crash, audible over the howling of the wind and the crashing of the waves. The ship suddenly lurched and stopped its pitching so abruptly that both men lost their footing and fell to the deck. The boat then adopted a decidedly different rocking motion accompanied by the screeching crunch of tortured timbers.

"Well, Chief, so much for a sandy beach. I'm afraid we're aground on the Chocolay Shoal."

The Chocolay Shoal is a rock reef about three quarters of a mile or so off the mouth of the Chocolay River. The Kershaw had struck the reef amidships and was now hung there while the seas continued to pound her against the jagged rock.

"Chief, where's your engine room crew?"

"They're all in the after cabin, to a man. When the line blew there was no further need for them to remain below. Luckily no one was badly injured in the explosion. A couple burns but none serious."

"Keep 'em there. I'll send the deck crews back there too. It's the safest place to be. You keep order and maintain their spirits as best you can. We're well within sight of Marquette Life Saving Station and those fellas are good. I'm going forward to keep the flares going. Good luck, Chief."

"You too, Captain."

The life saving crew was on the road with the surfboat and the wagon. They had about five miles to go and no idea what they might find when they got there. Whatever they encountered they felt they would be up to the task.

Back aboard the "Kershaw" the last of the flares had been expended and the entire fourteen-man crew was assembled in an after cabin. The Captain briefed the crew on what had occurred. "The ship's aground, I believe, on Chocolay Shoal, three quarters of a mile off shore. I don't know how long she'll last taking this hammering but she's a stout ship. This is the safest place for us to be. It's," he pulled out his watch and squinted at it in the dim lantern light, "right about 3:00 AM. In four or five hours it should be breaking daylight. We can decide then what to do next. 'Til then," he grinned at his crew, "smoke if ya got it. If you don't, watch me." There was a weak chuckle from the assembled men who recognized the remark.

The Captain's quip was an old saw used by instructors while recruits were going through training. During the rigorous drills the instructor might announce a break with, "OK! Ten minutes! Smoke if ya got it. If you don't, watch me." It did serve to relieve the tension just a little.

The hull of the "Kershaw" rocked and twisted and groaned as the Chocolay Shoal ground relentlessly at her stout timbers. The sea, the unforgiving sea gave no quarter. It steadily and continuously pounded the stricken ship. The men, jolted with each wave, waited inside the hull. There was nothing else they could do. They waited.

The lifesavers took approximately 45 minutes to reach the mouth of the Chocolay River. They stopped and watched and waited, straining to see or hear anything that would help them determine the location of the stricken ship.

The Station Chief sent men off along the shoreline in both directions looking for survivors, wreckage, whatever they might find. His instructions were, "Don't be gone more than an hour. Report back here with whatever you did - or did not find. We've got to have that information so don't forget to get word back. My guess, from what I saw from the tower, is that we'll find 'em east of here. We'll stay here in case they fetched up on the Chocolay Shoal. If they're on the beach – well – they're on the beach. OK, go! Be back here," he looked at his watch, "by five-thirty. It ought to be daylight soon after that."

Word of a ship in trouble had spread through town, even at this early hour. People were arriving, lining the beach to see what was happening. They congregated in small groups, started fires, watched and waited.

Aboard the hull of the Kershaw one of the men called out, "Captain! Captain!" pointing toward shore, "There a fire ashore."

The Captain looked. Sure enough there was a fire – no – more than one. There were several fires on shore. "Get a lantern! Let's show a lantern. They must have come by land and are searching the beach. Let's give 'em a light so they'll know we're here."

The shore parties had returned at 5:30 or there abouts. They had found both the "Moonlight" and the Kent" washed up relatively undamaged on the sand beach. The lifesaver crew immediately recruited some of the spectators to return down the beach to the two vessels. No one on either of the crews had been injured. They had almost been able to step ashore while hardly getting wet.

Suddenly several of the assembled group pointed and called to the lifesavers. "Look! Look! There's a lantern showing out there." Immediately the life savers began unloading their surfboat and moving it to the lake shore.

Dawn was beginning to break in the east as they prepared their craft for launching. The surf was still running very high and the wind and seas had not diminished. Further complicating the operation was the wreckage from the disintegrating "Kershaw" along with other logs and debris churned up by the storm.

The surfboat, like a lifeboat, is a self-bailing craft but not as heavy or as sturdy as a lifeboat. Now, with the boiling surf and the pounding debris, the surfboat itself could be in peril.

Several times the crew attempted to launch their craft into the tumultuous surf and several times it was driven back on the beach. It's not the number of times a person falls that decide a struggle; it's the number of times they rise again. The crew was well trained in these procedures and was not discouraged by the difficulty. This Station Master had achieved notoriety for being persistent – and successful.

The crew at last made it out past the breaking surf. Under the watchful eye and steadying hand of their commander the disciplined crew stroked steadily against the raging sea. The boat threaded its way through the floating debris, overcoming the gray walls of water bearing down upon them. Maneuvering the craft to the stricken "Kershaw" and holding its position beneath the stern of the stranded ship was an outstanding feat of seamanship.

Aboard the "Kershaw" spirits rose. "They're coming! They're coming! There's a boat put out from shore. Look at those guys. My God, how did they do it?"

The Captain lined up the men and established an order for recovery. He, the Captain, would be last to leave. The Chief Engineer elected to stay with him. First to go would be married men with priority given to those who had children. With that settled, they watched and waited.

Once the surfboat was positioned below the lurching stern of the ship the problem became one of getting aboard the wildly pitching craft. One by one the men, in order of selection, lowered themselves by rope. They hung there 'til the surfboat was positioned directly under them. As they let go willing hands stood ready to assist them. When nine of the fourteen-man crew were aboard the surfboat it was necessary to cast off. The small boat could hold no more without greater danger of swamping.

Delicately retracing its route the small boat fought its way back through the debris to shore. Landing was just as difficult as the launching. Several men had to jump over the side to fend off wreckage. One of the crew, caught between a broken timber and the hull of the surfboat, was injured.

The Captain, the Chief Engineer, and three seamen had remained aboard the "Kershaw." One of the seamen was the young recruit who had delivered the message for "more power." The five men braced themselves against the pounding of the reef and waited.

Ashore a volunteer was quickly selected from among the many volunteers to replace the injured crewman. Repeated attempts to launch finally led to success. Slowly they battled once more through the heavy seas and floating debris. With recovery of the remaining five crewmen within their grasp a sudden shift of the sea rolled the surfboat completely over. The crew, trained in the procedure, righted the craft - only to have it roll over again. Perseverance and training paid off and the craft was righted again but it had been struck and severely damaged by floating debris. They reluctantly elected to return to shore.

The return was not accomplished without incurring two more injuries. Once ashore the Station Master immediately set out for the Life Saving Station to get the larger, heavier lifeboat. Two more volunteers were obtained from among the spectators.

Out on the reef the battered "Kershaw" broke in half. The bow section was immediately washed away. The stern, housing the five survivors, shifted precariously. The remaining crewmembers had to re-establish their position to the lee side of the battered hulk and tie themselves on with ropes. As the stern shifted even more the men scrambled to secure a safer position – except for the young recruit. He remained, head bowed, clinging to a timber of the stricken craft.

"Come on, young fella, come on! Bear a hand," the Captain shouted. "What're you doin'?"

The young man looked up, terror stricken. "I'm praying, Captain, I'm praying."

"Listen," the Captain shouted sternly, "at sea we pray to God – but we row for shore. This is a time to be rowin'." The boy shifted his position and the five men hung on. They would be there for three more hours.

The lifesavers weren't able to return with the heavier lifeboat until 1:00 PM. The seas had abated slightly and, although debris and breaking waves continued to hamper their efforts, the crew and their three volunteers succeeded with the launching. They worked their way out through the surf to reach the side of the wreck. The remaining five crewmen, the Captain last, were recovered into the lifeboat and taken to shore.

The "Moonlight" and the "Kent" were later freed from the shore, refloated, salvaged and returned to service. The "Charles J. Kershaw" was a total loss.

The crews of the vessels, true seamen in every sense of the word, all returned to service aboard ships on the Great Lakes. The young seaman who had remained aboard with his Captain made a point of thanking him for his learned counsel in time of stress. "Thank you, sir," the lad said, "for a steadying hand and that wise counsel: 'Pray to God, but row for shore.' I'll certainly remember that."

Although there had been several injuries none were serious and no lives were lost. The rescue was a tribute to the professionalism of the seamen and the training and ability of the professional crew of the Marquette Life Saving Station. To a man they credited their capable Station Commander. And that live saving crew? They, too, stayed in the business. They're now called the United States Coast Guard and they're still good at what they do.

If any of you are divers, go visit the sandy bottom of the big lake in the vicinity of Chocolay Shoal. There are still bits and pieces of the wreckage of the "Charles J. Kershaw" down there. No "bones," but there's wreckage.

♎

THE LOGGERS

Introduction

The following chapters, The Trees, The Shanty Boys, The River Hogs, and The Walkin' Boss, are an overview of the men who developed and made a living from our forests. They're intended to provide a little insight into the forestry industry and how it has developed. It tries to envelop the evolution of logging, the economic gains which motivated it, the hardships endured by the early woods workers and the emergence of consideration for the natural resource that made it all possible. Radical opinions in both directions (we're fortunate if there only seem to be two) have become a way of life in our free society. That's a good thing. All opinions, ideas, objections should be brought out into the open where they can be examined and discussed. Hopefully this will result in compromise, common ground within which everyone can agree. If not, it can be decided by "disinterested third parties" or by a vote – majority rules.

It is doubtful if a flower child will ever go into the woods with a chain saw nor will a logger be apt to be found tending wild posies. If the knee-jerk response to oppose one another can be overcome we all may be able to sit down over a cup of coffee and compromise to keep spikes out of saw logs and preserve the natural order also. With good faith on both sides, we CAN have our cake - and eat it too.

♎

The Loggers

White Pine

White Pine was the much sought after prize of the North Woods. This example of the "old days" measures 17' in circumference, 6' in diameter.

The Trees

Where and how it all begins. The forest is just

like a farm with crops, livestock, and cycles of life. It's born, it lives, it dies and is replaced - just like you and I. It all begins with – “The Trees.”

This is a nonprofessional (underline that) analysis of where commercial logging begins - and how. Our forests are a gigantic farm with growing crops, livestock and cycles of life. As with all living things it's born, it lives and it dies - just like you and I. Like you and I it makes a contribution – or not. We and the trees can help or hurt each other along the way; it’s pretty much up to us.

The best guess by people who study such things is that 9,000 or 10,000 years ago (give or take a couple weeks) the last great glacier to cover the north central region of the United States, the Great Lakes region, melted and receded northward. This mass of ice had originated further north, moved southward gouging and grinding over the terrain. It dug the basins that would become the Great Lakes. It pulverized rocks chewing them into soil and depositing it in hollows and lower areas. Some became sandwiched between itself and the rocky undersurface. This process left scratches, scars, and striations across the face of the protruding rocks and mountains that are readily visible yet today.

As conditions changed the ice melted. The face on the glacier receded to the north. As the years passed the physical structure of the environment changed. The terrain as we know it slowly took shape. Seeds were blown here by the wind or carried in by birds that then excreted them due to their incomplete digestive process. A few, no doubt, arrived tangled in the fur or carried in the excrement of wandering wildlife. These seeds found root in the soil and began to grow. Imbedded nutrients, the depth of the soil, wind, rain and the weather nurtured some seedlings and rejected others. The plants that survived were strong and hardy and claimed a place in the sun. That environment determined what birds and animals would populate the area. It didn't happen overnight. It didn't happen over several years. It took several hundred years for our northland to arise from barren ice and rock into the woods and the water and the wildlife we enjoy today.

The early forest would have been composed of quick-growing trees called "pioneer" trees. The pioneer growth would have been composed of trees such as aspen, birch, and pin cherry that sprang up in the open, sunny, accommodating soil. Ferns, bracken, berry bushes and ground cover would blanket the forest floor. The trees would rapidly dominate the area shading the surface while providing food and cover for grouse, porcupine, beaver, moose, deer, and other wildlife. Aspen, locally called popple, is a rapid growing tree – up to three or four feet in a single season. In open areas it beats out competing growth. Once this growth is established its shade suppresses competing trees. It doesn't kill them but it does slow their growth considerably. This mixture provides a forest density in which a wildlife community forms.

Aspen are a prolific and very unique specie. It spreads through cotton-tufted easily blown seeds light enough to travel great distances. This seeding occurs among the mature trees every three to five years. Aspen also spread a vast root system, roots from which new growth also sprouts and spreads roots. These root systems may spread out for miles. A chemical substance released by mature trees further controls new growth. This chemical falls to the ground and suppresses new growth. It's a kind of automatic pruning system. The outcome is that the forest is not a jungle of young shoots exhausting the soil but a healthy stand of mature and maturing trees.

Pioneer growth will mature in from 30 to 60 years. The trees may attain 40 to 50 feet of height with a trunk 10 to 12 inches in diameter. At this stage the trees begin to die: In aspen particularly heart rot - the decay at the center of a mature tree – will weaken the trunk. A combination of this weakening and wind and weather will fell the tree. The tree will be re-absorbed into the soil as humus that will be recycled by providing fertilizer for new growth.

While this is going on another family of trees, called climax trees, have also been seeding the forest floor. This new climax forest grows more slowly. It bides its time surviving in the shaded environment under pioneer growth. When a large pioneer tree falls the break in the forest canopy increases the amount of light reaching the forest floor. This increased light accelerates the growth of the climax trees. Climax trees, balsam, white spruce, maple, basswood, beech, and pine for example, will move up to take over the area vacated by the pioneer growth. A climax forest lives longer than the pioneer forerunners. They will claim the area in their turn but at a much slower pace. Many of these climax trees number their lives in hundreds of years. Their shade will also suppress new growth, especially the growth of the shade intolerant pioneer trees. The seedlings of the climax forest will continue to sprout in this shaded environment. They will grow at a very slow pace, biding their time, awaiting their opportunity to take their place in the sun. Most will never survive to see that day. This is part of the cycle of life of a forest.

The wildlife that inhabits this forest, the birds and animals, will have adjusted to these changes. Those not able to adapt will either move on or perish becoming food for those who can. It's a system called evolution, survival of the fittest. In addition factors other than growth and re-growth affect a forest. Forest fires can be started by lightning, the sun shining through a broken bottle, a careless human may level large areas of mature forest. The cycle then starts again. A note for those who may be interested, a year or two after a forest fire drop by the area with a blueberry-picking bucket in hand. You won't be disappointed.

A jack pine tree is a pioneer tree that enjoys a special adaptation to forest fires. Frequently a fast moving forest fire will sweep through a stand of healthy jack pine with only superficial damage to mature trees. In a further quirk of nature the seed bearing cones of the jack pine tend to remain tightly closed until they are subjected to high temperature. This heating can occur while the cone lies on the ground under a hot summer sun - or it can happen during a forest fire. This glimpse - and I want to emphasize it is only a glimpse- of the natural forces which form the world in which we live has got to humble any observer who pauses to wonder.

Climax pine trees, "softwoods," (needle leafed trees), are a repetition of their hardwood cousins. They, too, will mature becoming a tall dominant pine forest. Their cathedral-like canopy can be awe-inspiring as a person stands in the dense shade created on the forest floor. Pine needles - they are really pine "leaves," long slender green leaves - age, die, and drop to the ground like their broad-leaf cousins. They do not do this seasonally. Pine needles are continuously sprouting, growing, dying, and dropping to the forest floor. The pine needles decay much more slowly than the "deciduous" leaves and they are much more acidic. These unique factors combine to smother new growth and generate a soil in which only other pine growth will prosper. The vegetation which sends roots through the soil also serves to anchor the soil against washing away in rain or snow melt thereby stabilizing the whole environment.

Camping among these aged giants is a humbling experience. An older, mature pine forest conveys the aura of a church, a cathedral – with a complete absence of the hypocrisy that often seems associated with man made counterparts. Alone among these ancient giants in a silent world a person feels dwarfed by a stature that's hundreds of years old. There can be a feeling of confinement in a primal night and restricted to the small globe of firelight surrounding your campsite. Burning wood snaps and crackles busily. Shadows, like woodland spirits, leap and dance all about. Huge tree trunks stand watching, silent and impersonal. Anyone not awed in these surroundings by their own insignificance has lost contact with their soul.

A small stream murmurs and chortles at the edge on the light. The night wind sighs through the branches high above - or moans, depending on your mood. It's a silent overwhelming wonder secluded and away from the hustle and bustle of a modern world. The words of a verse I once painted on the cowl of a sailboat I owned seem to apply here also: "Thy sea is so great. My boat is so small."

Most of the old growth giants of the forest are gone. There are a few scattered stands left - at the tip of the Keweenaw Peninsula, a few on lands owned by a private club. Those old timers of the forest are homes to the ghosts of the lumberjacks, the "shanty boys" who cut down their brothers. All have passed on into the shadowy folds of a history which itself is fading away.

A new breed of woodsman has arisen along with a new management culture; "tree farming." The intertwining forces of men, trees and nature surge back and forth in the unending struggle that will determine the evolutionary path we will follow.

> *"Your destiny is a mystery. . . what will happen when the secret corners of the forest are heavy with the scent of man . . .? Where will the thicket be? Gone! And what is it to say good by . . .? It is the end of living and the beginning of survival. . . Man (will have) vanished with his wilderness and his memory only the shadow of a cloud. . ."*

Seattle, Chief,
Suquamish tribe;
1786 - 1866

The Loggers

Superior View Studios photo, Marquette, MI

Camp Breakfast

Up, fed and out in the woods before daybreak. Eat your fill! No talkin' at the table. Good lumber camps fed the men well.

The "Shanty Boys"

Shanty Boys is what they called them before the label "lumberjack" became popular. In the early days life was hard and so was working in the woods. It is still one of the most hazardous of occupations. The majority of those early profits went to bankers back east. Those banks, after all, were where the initial investments came from. On the other end of the operation the shanty boy's investment was blood, sweat, and life under very primitive conditions. Their life in the woods was very basic. They worked hard, walked tall, dove deep, swung a broad ax, and helped build a nation. They had names like "Moonlight" Johnson, Big Eric, Tom "Tin-Can" Sullivan, Silver Jack Driscol, "Good Lookin' Tom," "Ten O'clock Charlie," Big Bill Bonifas, and there were others.

"Moonlight" Johnson was "The Push," the woods foreman. He was famous for rousing his crews in the dark, feeding them by lamplight, and getting them to the woods, ready to start cutting at first light.

"Tin Can" Sullivan wasn't always the happiest of employees and would often refer to the operation he was involved with as a "Tin Can" outfit. Another story is that around his bachelor's shack in the woods could be found the rusting food cans he had casually tossed out the door. Another more somber tale involved Tom arranging his cabin with a candle on a tin can partially filled with and surrounded by sprinkled lamp oil. Tom set up this "fusing" device, so they say, and then shot himself in his cabin. Tom's buried in the local "Potter's Field." His fire/fusing device didn't work.

"Good Lookin' Tom" Procyk was a refugee from Russia who once worked at the local "Granot Loma" lodge. The owner's wife, to differentiate between two Toms who worked for her gave him the name "Good Lookin' Tom."

"Ten O'clock Charlie" was a young fella who worked in the woods during the "rubber tired" logging days. These were the early automobile days of lumberjacks living at home and driving to the woods to work. Instead of being in the woods at first light Charlie was usually a bit late. He was apt to show up more like ten o'clock or so. The story was that he hadn't been married long, had a very attractive young wife, and – well – many mornings he didn't get to work 'til 10 o'clock.

These guys were all a product of the times they lived in and most have passed on to that great stand of timber in the sky. They're missed. We're not apt see their like again.

The identity of the first folks who wandered through Michigan's Upper Peninsula is lost in the dim dark days beyond recall. The sheet of ice that gripped the land receded some 10,000 years ago – give or take a week or two. Let's say that 3,000 years ago (and who really knows) someone was here digging up copper. Who? I don't know. Maybe it was the Egyptians. They were big on copper. The Indians lived here off and on. "Native Americans" is the current politically correct title. It was Columbus in 1492 that laid the title "Indian" on them and it's pretty well established that he didn't know where he was or who these people were. These people were a nomadic people, wanderers. It wasn't until the early 1600s that a Frenchman, Etienne Brule, the first white man we have any real knowledge of, saw the mighty Lake Superior. After that, well, the Indians will tell you, there went the neighborhood.

The early occupants didn't use the trees, the woods, for much but tools and campfires and to hunt in. The Indians used saplings, young trees as supports for their skin and or bark covered shelters. As with some of the current dwellers in the north country, when the weather turned cold the Indians went south – not to Florida or Texas or Arizona but at least as far as Bay de Noc on Lake Michigan.

About 1831 with the continuing influx of the white man a fella named William Farnsworth built a small sawmill at the mouth of the Menominee River where it emptied into Lake Michigan's Bay De Noc. Unfortunately he was a little ahead of his time and the venture failed.

Around 1860 a guy named George Dawson discovered the big pine along Lake Superior's south shore and began cutting near what is now the Big Bay area just east of the Huron Mountains. He and his men cut down large trees with axes, squared them with a sharp grub-hoe looking tool called an adze. They then shipped them, floated them actually, to his brother, Thomas, who was at Sault Ste Marie on the eastern tip of Lake Superior. Thomas would trans-ship the timbers to England, mostly for shipbuilding. These were the days when "Britannia ruled the waves" and she needed the timbers to build the ships.

Dawson and his logging crew were pretty much restricted to cutting trees that were near the water. They had no way to move the logs except by floating them. Meanwhile, back on the east coast, American loggers were chewing their way through the forests of the New England states, New York and Pennsylvania. As the land was cleared they followed the big trees west. By the 1870s these loggers were into the Lower Michigan area and were moving into the Upper Peninsula and Wisconsin.

The ax was their primary tool. Saws had been in use one way or another since the Roman era but they didn't work very well especially on large pieces of wood. The rough cutting edge, the "teeth," tended to jam up with woodcuttings, the sawdust and that would hinder the cutting. It wasn't 'til the 1880s that the tooth sequence of what would become the crosscut saw was modified. Who did this? I would guess it was probably some "shanty boy" trying to figure a better way to do the job. Whoever it was, they added a "tooth" without a cutting edge, square and blunt and slightly shorter than the cutting teeth. With the addition of these "rakers" between the cutting teeth the sawdust would be raked along with the moving blade. As these rakers reached the end of the kerf, the saw cut, the sawdust dropped out. This eliminated the sawdust jamming the teeth and the crosscut saw came into wide use in the woods. The lumberjacks used to refer to the long two-man crosscut saw as "misery whips." You can probably figure that one out yourself.

Another problem that arose with crosscut saws, particularly with the pine trees, was the pitch in the wood that would adhere to the blade. The men pounded wedges into their back-cuts to keep the kerf from squeezing the saw and binding. They also carried small containers of kerosene that normally fueled the camp lights. They would squirt or sprinkle kerosene on the saw blade to eliminate the build up of pitch. A logger in the northern woods was a pretty self-contained unit. If they couldn't figure a way out of the problem, there was no way out of the problem. The guy who was clever enough to solve these problems often became "the push" – the woods boss.

It was eastern money, primarily the Boston area that financed the logging in the Midwest. These eastern speculators hired land lookers to "cruise" the new land and select choice stands of timber which they, the speculators, then bought, sold and traded.

There was darned little law in the deep woods. That didn't arrive 'til the settlements and the railroads.

Lumber barons often just moved in, cut the timber and moved out. Later the expression became to "cut a round forty." They would purchase a forty-acre tract, cut it, and cut all the forties around it. It was sort of understood that the land belonged to the government but the government wasn't very well represented in the backwoods.

Some of the land lookers, the timber cruisers recognized the opportunities and bought a bit of that action themselves. It was widely believed that many early "developers" stole more than just a little bit. Much government land was just cut off, period, and nothing was ever done about it. Who was there to complain? There was a lot of wheelin' and dealin' and stealin' all up and down the line. The guys with the axes and the saws were usually on the short end of the stick. They got "room," as basic as it was, and "board," the camps usually fed well lest the whole crew leave for better vittles, but darn little for their labor. The money went back east.

The fellas who were workin' six days a week from sunup to sundown were the lumberjacks, the Shanty Boys. They were generally a poorly educated happy-go-lucky bunch who were used to a hard life. They had long ago learned to take the good with the bad and few looked any farther ahead than the next payday. They worked hard, drank heavy, jumped high, dove deep, ran fast, and bragged that they could whip anybody in the house. The life was hard, the pay was poor ($12 to $15 a month), and lucky was the man who avoided injury. Yeah, they took the good with the bad - mostly bad. The boss, "the push," got 'em up before daylight so they'd be in the woods as soon as it was light enough to work. Lunch, they called it "dinner," was brought out to the job. "Supper" is what you got back at the camp and they didn't get back to camp 'til after dark.

Sundays were "a day off." That's what it was called. It was time spent repairing clothing, mending and sharpening equipment, and trying to chase the cooties, the "mechanized dandruff" out of clothing and the bedding - such as the bedding was. A "sheet" was something involved with higher-class outhouses.

Bunkhouses were designed to accommodate the maximum number of men. The men often slept two to a bunk. If the bunks were parallel to the wall, entered from the side, they were called "Breech loader." If they were close-packed, head-against-the-wall, they were entered from the end and called "muzzle loaders." Two guys in one bunk would be separated one from another by a "snortin' pole" down the center of the bunk.

An evening's intellectual discussion might take place from the "deacons seat," a seat near the stove. The conversation might speculate on the merits of avoiding a bath on the theory that the smell would keep the mosquitoes away. These were hard livin' men. They sweat, they swore, they told tall tales, and they cut timber from dawn 'til dark all for $12 to $15 a month "and found." "And found" meant those bunks shared with the cooties and "three square meals" a day. No talking at the table and usually only one – albeit a large one – piece of pie per man. The cook had planned it that way and woe be to whoever crossed the cook.

Some of the "jacks were family men and sent a good bit of their pay to their families. In the early days life was too primitive to have families in the woods. When the men got to town – town was wherever there was a bar - they hollered and they drank and they spent what money they had. Their work involved hard labor, physical strength and that was how they measured one another. The booze they drank washed away inhibitions. Arguments tended to be settled physically. They fought - one another if there was no one else around. Lumberjacks were the cowboys of the North Country. They didn't receive the publicity that attended their southwestern cousins. There weren't many reporters or public relations people in the woods.

As railroads stretched their bands of steel into the logging country they began to replace horses and oxen. Rail lines would branch out from the main line into the timber country. They'd lay railroad tracks into a stand of timber, cut the timber and haul it out, then pick up the track, and lay 'em down in the next stand. Sometimes the railroad cars became portable lumber camps. They would be enclosed and lined with bunks and a stove. Another car might be made into a cook shanty with another one or two as the dining hall.

In the 1930s and 40s an era of "rubber tired-logging" began. Trucks were able to take the place of in-the-woods railroads for the short hauls. Automobile prices were low enough that a workingman could afford to buy one, albeit second hand. This made it possible for some of the men, those with family nearby, to live at home and commute to the woods. As farms and settlements populated the cleared land it became common for summertime farmers to hire on cutting timber during the winter months. Both occupations tended to be seasonal and they fit each other rather well.

In the 1940s, during World War II, German prisoners of war were sent to the UP to work in the woods. Much to their surprise the government discovered it had to have special quarters built for the prisoners. The rules of the Geneva Convention governing treatment of prisoners of war considered the living conditions in the lumber camps below the minimum standards required.

Working in the woods was and still is a dangerous occupation. There's always the hazard of falling trees. A logger learns to watch for dead falls, a dead tree which falls but become hung-up in the fork of another tree - "widow-makers," they're called.

They can break free and fall at any time. Then there are shifting logs, broken towlines and binders, all are part of the job. The food was plentiful and almost universally good - plain but good. Nothing would send a man down the road to another camp faster than poor food.

Logging camp operators sometimes had to hire "man-catchers," recruiters who traveled to the cities to recruit men to work in the woods. These new guys, many unacquainted with work in the woods, might show up in fancy oxfords and city clothes to work in the northern woods - in winter. The "push," the boss, would meet the guys coming in and gather the newcomer's sacks, bags, suitcases. "For safekeeping," he said. Yeah, safekeeping! It was for keeping his recruits safe and available to work.

Experiencing the north woods in winter often set these newcomers to wondering why they ever left home. The thinking was that they weren't apt to leave if their gear was locked up and they had nothing but the clothes on their backs. Many left anyway with just the clothes on their backs.

It was customary for the men to work all winter, collect their poke after the spring log drive, and head for town. In a week or so many would have gotten drunk, "blew it in" as they called it, spent or had their money stolen, and they'd straggle back to the woods. They'd be broke but with wild tales to tell during their turn in the deacon's seat. They were ready to do it all over again. There were exceptions - but not many. This was the life of a "Shanty Boy."

A German fella' invented the chain saw in 1937. It would be many years before it was made light enough and portable enough to use in the woods. By the 1940s the gasoline engine was replacing horses and oxen. The pulpwood and chemical wood market was replacing the market for saw logs (the big timber was becoming scarce) and bowling pins (they were making them of plastic).

Chemical wood could be a smaller log than those used for lumber. It can even be partially rotted wood. The processing of chemical wood involves heating the wood above its burning temperature but enclosing it in an airtight container. The smoke and fumes are captured and condensed to recover wood alcohol and other marketable chemicals. The remaining charcoal would be ground up and used for various processes including the charcoal briquettes which many people use in outdoor barbecues.

Pulpwood involves wood of almost any size that is first stripped of its bark, then it's literally torn apart and recombined to manufacture paper – which our computer printers eat in ever increasing quantities.

Lumberjacks, those who stayed because of age or whatever, when their brothers moved west following the big timber, would often get work "cuttin' pulp" for a season. In the fall a "jobber" would hire them. He'd provide them with "a stake," bacon, beans, coffee, a little salt, a little tobacco. The man would then live alone in a small cabin – or tarpaper shack - in the woods through the winter. He would cut the pulpwood to eight-foot lengths and peel the bark. These days the paper mills remove the bark mechanically, they perform the bark peeling process. In the old days the old 'jack would earn anywhere from three to five cents a stick, payable when the jobber returned and took an inventory in the spring. The cost of the previous fall's grubstake would be deducted, of course.

Those old time pulp cutters are a disappearing breed. They may be in nursing homes, veteran's hospitals; there may be a few still living by themselves. They're the last of that tall walkin', loud talkin', deep drinkin', hard fightin' bunch. They've been left behind, outdated like old and worn out tools, cast aside like an empty container. Names like "Moonlight" Johnson, Silver Jack Driscol, "Tin Can" Sullivan, Big Jack and Ten O'clock Charlie, John the Bull and there were many others. They've faded into the mists of a disappearing past. The world is not likely to see their kind ever again.

A modern day logger has arisen. There's a new breed of "Shanty boy." The cross cut saw and the broad ax have given way to the mechanized feller-buncher, the rubber-tired hydraulic skidder, the multi-armed slasher. "Eastern Money" has become "The Corporation" and may still be mainly in the east. The jobber/lumberjack of today may well be a small business unto himself. Self-employed or managing a small crew he will contract with larger businesses. He needs a quick mind as well as a strong back. He's got to be able to negotiate with a banker as well as swear at the crew. He can't throw his Pettibone loading machine over his shoulder and head down the road as easily as the old 'jack could his ax. In addition to doing his own timber cruising he has to estimate cutting time, schedule equipment maintenance, calculate profit margins, estimate returns on investment, understand the effect of interest rates, taxes, insurance.

Ah, but if you ask him if he'd do it again, he'll look at you - kind of sideways, you know - and maybe rub the back of his neck. He'll probably kick the dirt, maybe spit, and then he'll admit it. "Yeah, yeah, I probably would." Then he'll sneak a look to see if you're laughin' at him. The thing is they love the woods, most of them. They really do. They're out there every day. They're their own boss. They can cuss when they want to, scratch where it itches, and they're in the woods. And that's where they want to be.

I enjoy the woods myself. I guess that's why I like those loggers – those shanty boys.

♎

The Loggers

Superior View Studios photo, Marquette, MI

Hazardous Work

Good balance, quick wits and nimble feet were the requirements for a river driver. They earned more than the slightly higher pay they received.

The River Hogs

These were the cream of the cream, the proud men who literally rode the timber to market. In the early days there were no railroads or trucks or roadways. Skidding was done on iced winter trails with horses and mules and oxen. Logs, stacked on riverbanks, were floated to market on the spring flood. There was no workmen's compensation or unemployment benefits or hospitalization. Life was an existence on the edge of disaster. It wasn't 'til much later that railroads, and roads, and rubber-tired trucks and mechanization came along to ease that part of the task. These days the guys who used to jump from one bucking log to another floating timber are instead balancing insurance costs against operating expenses while searching for hauling contracts - and he can still drown if he slips.

As we mentioned before it was 1860 when George Dawson and his brother, Thomas, started the first serious timber cutting along the south shore of Lake Superior north of Marquette. They were selective in choosing large trees that could be squared into timbers and shipped to England to build ships. As large and as heavy as these timbers were they were difficult to move. This limited their selections to trees that could be cut so as to fall into or near the water. Moving these large timbers on land would have been extremely difficult. They had to be able to float them.

By 1880 more expansive loggers had arrived. Farsighted speculators and woodsmen like Timothy Nestor, Charles Hebard, Bill Bonifas, Jim Redi, and John Longyear quickly recognized the potential in the area. They saw the wealth that was there for the taking.

The forest soon echoed with the whack of axes. Recognizing their limitations they timed their cutting to take advantage of the seasons. Horses and oxen could move logs more easily along iced trails. Cutting was done with an eye to moving the logs during the winter. In winter when nights were colder, and on Sundays, times when the trails weren't being used, a sled carrying a tank filled with water would be pulled up and down the trails sprinkling water to ice the trails. Teamsters and their teams would pull single logs to these iced skidding trails, put several logs together and skid them to a holding area. The holding area might be next to a larger iced trail or tote road. Here they'd "deck," stack the logs to be loaded on sleighs and hauled to a river. There the logs would be "decked" on the riverbank in anticipation of the spring flood.

Many of these rivers were too small to float logs by themselves so dams would be constructed along these waterways. A fundamental rule is that you cannot "stop" water. You can drink it, slow it, divert it but that water cannot be stopped. The idea for the dams is that they would be large enough to hold up the spring run-off. This would store a large "head" of water with enough force and volume to carry pine logs downstream to a predetermined destination. This only worked for pine. Hardwood, deciduous trees – those with leaves - were too heavy to be floated easily.

Preparations for these spring drives would involve clearing the river downstream of deadfalls, brush, and protruding rocks, of anything that might hinder the passage of the logs or that could develop into a potential trouble spot. The dam-augmented water flow would have a finite and relatively short life. Eliminating as many problems as possible before hand helped to assure a maximum number of logs would make it to the assembly areas down stream.

When all was in readiness the logs were rolled into the water, the water and logs would be released through a sluiceway, and it was "Katy, bar the door!" Depending on the amount of water available it might be planned with a sudden rush sweeping the logs before it or more controlled rate moving at a slower rate for a longer time. It all depended upon the natural flow of the river itself, the amount of water contained and the judgment of the "push," the woods boss.

There would normally be at least three crews of drivers or "River Hogs." Men chosen had to be strong, quick thinking, have good balance, and endurance. The job paid an additional 50 cents a day so volunteers were plentiful. These River Hogs wore "calked" boots, boots whose soles had half or three quarter inch steel spikes embedded in them to give the man as firm a footing as possible. The drivers would carry pike poles or peaveys for balance and to keep the logs aligned, free and moving along.

The pike pole was just a long stick with a spike and a spur on the end to push or pull the floating logs. A peavey was a shorter and stouter pole with a swinging arc shaped hook a foot or two long attached to a pivot a foot or two up the handle. This allowed a person to swing the hook out, dig the heavy barbed end into a log and use the leverage of the handle to pry or roll the log. There are two names for this tool; "Peavey," named for the fella who invented it, or "Cant Hook" determined by the spike or spike and barb on the foot, the bottom of the pole.

The first crew down the river had to be the most nimble. They rode the crest of the drive and had to keep the lead logs from jamming. They had to be quick witted and daring to head off trouble in that fast moving flood.

The next crew kept the following logs lined up and moving smoothly downstream. If the lead crew encountered a bad jam they might have to get word to the following crew to attempt to slow or stop the flow. This would be attempted by creating a log-boom - several logs chained together end-to-end and snubbed to stout trees on the banks. Hopefully this would trap most of the following logs and also slow down the flow of the stream. Once the jam was cleared the logs would again be released.

The third crew needed a lot of muscle. They would follow in the rear of the drive freeing logs that had become tangled in brush or grounded. They tried to get them back into deeper water and moving again before the water receded. The whole purpose was to get as many logs - all the logs if possible - down the river and to the market. There was no profit in a log stranded on the bank.

These were the "River Hogs," the men with the steel spikes in their "hob-nail" boots who jumped from log to bouncing log, riding a rolling raging torrent of water headed for the sea. This was the lumberjack equivalent of a cowboy's cattle drive aboard a bucking broncho and every bit as exciting as a stampede. If a man slipped, fell between the logs, well, that was usually that. There was no time to pause or look back. The river didn't stop and neither did anyone else.

Whatever time it took the water to run down stream, that's how long the men rode the river. They'd grab a bite to eat whenever and wherever they could. Any tangle or logjam had to be cleared - immediately! In the event of a bad logjam it took a brave man - or a fool, probably a little of both, to climb down the face of a jumble of logs with the sole intent of trying to make it fall on him.

The motivation of the River Hogs wasn't just the pay though. There was the attraction of being a member of that group, men whose strength, ability, and courage was a badge of courage, manhood. There was prestige that accompanied the job. It gave a man braggin' rights in the deacon's seat at camp. It might even get a free drink at the brass rail at a bar. "By gar! Ol' Ed here can drive a thousand footer (a thousand board feet of lumber - a big log) over wet grass." There'd be a shake of the head and a slap on the bar. "Set up a round of drinks over here!" And another jug of Hungry Hollow Moonshine sloshed down the gullets "fer the boys." A glass might be held high and an admirer would shout, "Here's to Ol' Ed!"

This admiration was often purchased at a high price. More than one of the drivers found their reward in a hole in the dirt on a riverbank. That is if they were lucky enough to find him. Maybe somebody'd say a few kind words - religious sounding if anyone could remember any.

There's an unobtrusive grave near the gate to the Huron Mountain Club just beyond Big Bay in Upper Michigan. It's on the west bank of the Salmon Trout River, on the right just over the bridge. There's a headstone: "Edward Martin, 1886." No one knew when he had been born. He and another river hog rode their last log that year. They slipped; fell under the crush of rushing logs. They might have drowned or they might have been crushed between logs – or both. The drive moved on. When it was over and the river had settled back into its banks some of the boys went back to look for them. They were lucky. They found Ed. They stuffed his feet into one barrel and covered his head with another. The makeshift coffin was lowered into a hole they dug on the riverbank. They might have hung his boots on a branch overhead – unless somebody else needed a pair that size. It was a somber moment. Kick the dirt, look at one another, "He leadeth me beside the still waters." Yeah! Well, I'm sure Ed's waters are still now - back to work.

It was years later that Ed Martin's relatives came down from up in Canada somewhere. It was they who arranged for the modest headstone. The guards who man the nearby Huron Mountain Club gatehouse keep the gravesite picked up, looking neat. If you're ever up that way, stop by. Now you know the story. Ed was one of the luckier ones. Many jacks had no one – or they had lost track of each other. How many don't have headstones – or somebody else needed their boots worse than they did. These, too, were men who built this country.

By 1900 local river drives were pretty much a thing of the past. The pine, what there had been of it, was mostly gone. There was still some hardwood but hardwood doesn't float very well. Kelly Beerman was a Big Bay native who worked at the "hot pond." The "hot pond" was where logs were assembled and fed to the "bull chain" that hauled them inside the sawmill. It was called "hot" because it was heated, usually by a steam pipe from the sawmill, so it wouldn't freeze in winter. One day a trucker drove up and dropped a load of beech logs into the water. "Dropped" was really the operative word. They were hardwood logs that wouldn't float. They went right to the bottom of the pond. "We had a h--l of a time gettin' 'em up again" Kelly remembered with a shake of his head.

When railroads snaked into the area about 1906 they were soon followed by "Limey" railroad engines, a Shay Patent Geared Locomotive. These smaller locomotives were powerful vertical-piston Shay-type steam engines. They were manufactured in Lima, Ohio, (hence the name "Limey") and soon became a workhorse of the woods. Crews would lay railroad tracks into a stand of timber. The trees would be cut, loaded and hauled out on railroad cars. When the marketable timber was gone the crew would pick up the tracks - sometimes in sections twenty or thirty feet long - and lay them into a fresh stand. A person wandering the woods yet today may still find a railroad spike in remote locations in the back woods.

The little Limey engine was famous far and wide for its high RPM (Revolutions Per Minute) engine and its slow speed. To hear it coming you'd think it was going ninety miles an hour. When it came 'round the bend it would be moving at about a fast walk. The high RPM and low speed gave it a lot of power. It's been said that, if they'd lay the tracks, it'd climb straight up the side of a tree

By the late 1930s and early 1940s rubber tired trucks and gasoline engines were replacing the railroads - just like the railroads had replaced the horses and oxen. This "rubber tire era" allowed many of the lumberjacks to live at home and commute to the woods. The days of the loggin' camps were fading too. One of the guys who commuted picked up the nickname "Ten O'clock Charlie." It was said he didn't show up for work 'til ten o'clock, rather than at daybreak like the rest of the crew. Charlie said it was because he was a truck driver and there were no logs to load 'til then. It was also said that, since he had only recently married a very pretty young lady and that they – well – that's another story for another day.

Chain saws, crawler tractors, and rubber-tired skidders soon found their place in the woods. With mechanization and hydraulics a tree can be cut, limbed, chopped, loaded, and delivered to the mill without ever being touched by a human hand.

Those river hogs haven't completely disappeared though. You can still see them today. They'll pass you on the highway in an "eighteen wheeler," - actually it probably has 42 wheels. They're still ridin' those logs – to the mill at Quinnesec or to Meade Paper Company at Escanaba - or maybe the mill at Sagola. He's probably an independent operator though, contract-hauling for a jobber who's contract cutting in the woods. He'll have a lot more invested in equipment than that guy who rode the river. The old time river hog didn't own anything but caulked boots and the shirt on his back. "The Company" owned his peavey or pike pole. His modern counterpart's truck alone is about $80,000 - plus the trailer - plus the "pup" (the trailer behind the trailer). This modern river hog has got to meet truck payments, figure interest rates, insurance costs and maintenance (each of the tires on those 42 wheels cost at least $250 - and the two front tires even more). Then there's the fuel cost. And he's got to line up hauling contracts. He'll probably rack up 100,000 miles on his rig in a year. Lessee, that'll be two sets of tires - how many miles per gallon? – And what about the hauling restrictions – you know - the spring load limits on the roads? – And then there's . . . Yes, the "River Hog" is still with us and if he's not quick witted he may "slip between the logs" too. "Ol' Ed" is still with us, still slippin' those thousand footers across quite a lot of wet grass.

The Loggers

Lake Independence Lumber Co.

Lumber, wood for automobiles, hardwood duck pins and bowling pins were the mainstay of this operation.

The Walkin' Boss

The company had a guy who traveled from camp to camp to monitor what was going on, to look after the company interests. He was "the walkin' boss." He represented why everything was happening, what logs would be cut, where they would go, who'd get paid – and how much. "The push" was the boss in the woods but he took his orders from the walkin' boss. It's when "the push" and "the walkin' boss" become too far removed, one from another, that we all get into trouble.

The Shanty Boys, the Lumber Jacks who cut the trees and the River Hogs who delivered the logs were mostly a down-to-dirt live-for-today bunch. They never seemed to get ahead, most of them, but they lived for today and the devil take tomorrow. They worked hard, drank deep, fought one another, and howled at the moon. Every season they did it all over again. Wear and tear and old age finally wore them out but it was a wild, woolly and colorful run while it lasted.

The forces at work in those days were the needs of a growing nation. We were building westward with the expansion financed by east-coast money. The financiers were from Boston, Pittsburgh, New York, and Cleveland. There's a motivation in human beings that inclines them toward self-interest, profit, greed. For all too many the motivation was profit! Even those who already had more than they could spend in a lifetime the profits were how they "kept score" in this game of life. Unfortunately this can become an all-consuming disease. It can be an all-consuming urge to make money and money and more money. Incidental to this lust they also helped to build a nation along the way.

Some of the men who came to Michigan's Upper Peninsula saw how profit making was being done. They recognized the motivating forces and harnessed them to their own advantage. They literally grabbed their own bootstraps and pulled themselves up into fame and fortune, men like John Longyear, Bill Bonifas and Charles Hebard - and there were others. They matched their vision with the resources available and an understanding of value. They joined the trek through the trees. Their quick judgment and shrewd management was carried along on the sweat and muscle of the shanty boys and the river hogs. They rode to fame and fortune on the rough bark of virgin timber.

The Indians who had been here all along didn't understand the ways of these newcomers, these white men. The Indians had no concept of "owning" land. The land was there. It belonged to everyone. As a result of their misunderstanding they gave away the land they had freely shared to a society based on self-interest, profit, acquisition and restriction. Treaties they didn't comprehend were signed for minimal benefits delivered as promises that all too often were rarely honored. And they were sold on the ethereal promises of the "black robes," the preachers, of a better life awaiting them in the hereafter. Be peaceful and submissive and all would be well by and by.

Upon receipt of the territory the new social order

scrambled to sell, transfer and convey title to timber and mineral interests to the profit-motivated newcomers who were destined to reshape the future. Some of these adventurers simply ignored the formality of the paperwork. They simply rushed into the territory treating the land as their own. There were few around to enforce the law and even fewer who seemed interested. The government itself didn't seem very concerned with the details. Men and supplies were brought in to erect camps, to provide the bare necessities to live and to work. The imported livestock often better cared for than the human beings. It was more difficult to replace a good horse than to find a couple lumberjacks.

Through all of this strode the "Walkin' Boss." He walked pretty tall through the timber as the symbol of the owners – and there was often more than one owner. He traveled from camp to camp checking on the stands of timber, what had been cut, the methods employed to assure the smooth flow of the logs to the sawmills. He oversaw the shipping of lumber on to market. He was the man who implemented the company's vision of the future.

Since it was also the company who brought in and sold the clothing, tobacco, and other necessities of life – the bare necessities I might add - to sustain the men the walkin' boss looked into those matters also. The company provided shelter such as it was, brought in the food, hired cooks, cookies and helpers and did whatever was necessary to keep the crews in the woods and working.

In the camps the men were almost always up before dawn. The plan was to feed them and have them in the woods ready to go as soon as it was light enough to work. If there was "daylight in the swamp," the boys were out there cutting trees. Dinner was brought to the worksite. Supper was eaten back at camp - after dark.

Sawmills were established on or near the mouth of a stream. The flowing water was used to carry the logs to the sawmill and to provide power for the sawmill through the use of a water wheel. A dam would often be constructed to raise the water level, providing a greater "drop" to furnish enough power to operate the mill.

In the very early days two men would cut lumber using an "Open Pit Saw." One man stood above and one stood in a pit below. The log would be fixed stationary on a bed. Human muscle furnished the power. The single vertical saw blade would be pulled up and down. Saw teeth were set to cut on the down stroke. This relieved the fella on top of having to raise the saw and cut wood also.

The next improvement was called the frame saw. A sort of window frame that minimized twisting and binding of the blade held the blade taut. The next development was the "Muley Saw." This saw incorporated a much heavier saw blade which would be operated, moved up and down by an external power source, a water wheel for example. The weight of this saw required more power than two men could provide. There were also "Gang" saws that incorporated several parallel saw blades mounted side by side in a large frame. It operated in the same up and down manner as the muley saw. The gang saw gained fame for the large amount of sawdust it created.

Circular saws replaced the bladed saws. The circular saw was a much simpler arrangement. A whirling toothed disk could cut continuously and was much more efficient. Later gasoline and diesel engines replaced steam power. Then came the band saw, a long, continuous band of steel in a loop. The band saw also cut continuously but, since the band saw blade was much thinner than the circular saw disk, it cut a much narrower "kerf."

The kerf is the width of the saw cut. The narrower the kerf, the more useable lumber could be had from the same size log. A 1/4" kerf on a circular saw would "waste" a 1" board every fourth cut: The 1/8" band saw kerf reduced that loss by half.

With sawmills located at or near the mouth of a river, ships could readily reach the site to transport the lumber to markets.

With the increasing efficiency of logging operations individual operators began forming partnerships. Partnerships merged and became corporations. Each combination led to more centralized control. Decisions were being made farther and farther from the physical resources, from the actual logging operation. Boards of directors narrowed their focus to the profit and loss statement. Concern for the conservation of natural resources were quickly set aside in favor of the bottom line of the income statement.

The big pine finally gave out. The remaining hardwood was useable for furnishing framework for automobiles (there was still a good bit of wooden construction in automobiles back then), bowling pins, furniture, and beautiful wood flooring. Even the cull trees, the less desirable wood, found a market in plants built to produce chemicals and manufacturing charcoal but the days of the big pine were gone.

The expansion of the paper industry gave birth to a growing demand for more and more pulpwood. Increasing publication of books, magazines, newspapers and the birth of computer printouts brought with them an increasing market demand for paper – and for the wood that produced it. We were soon consuming wood faster than we were growing it.

Early "forest management" was not management. The old philosophy had been cut-and-run. What was left – the nonmarketable wood referred to as "slashing" – was abandoned where it lay on the forest floor. The slashing quickly dried out and became very flammable. Too frequently this tinder was ignited by lightning, careless humans or maybe by sunlight magnified by a piece of broken glass. Whatever the reasons, the results were catastrophic forest fires. Once ignited and with any wind at all they were impossible to control. These roaring infernos would light the night sky in rose-colored hues. Whole towns were destroyed, Quinnesec, Talbot, Cornell, Ralph, Peshtigo. Firefighters could be trapped in a fast moving fire and burned to death. In 1906 the lakeside town of Munising was ringed by fire and thought to be doomed. A chance on-shore breeze from Lake Superior slowed the conflagration and fire fighters were able to save the city.

In 1903 the Cleveland Cliffs Company hired a forester, the first one ever, a Mr. S.M. Higgins. The need for consideration of the environment, for planned forestry had finally been recognized. By 1908 a fella named Thomas B. Wyman who had been hired as an assistant to Mr. Higgins started a formal forestry school; The Wyman School of the Woods. Progress was slow but it was progress.

The burgeoning paper industry was devouring more and more wood. The necessary investment in plant, equipment and the purchase of forestland dictated the economic need for long-range planning. The Mead Paper Company had invested in 700,000 acres in Michigan's Upper Peninsula. They soon recognized the advantage of converting this stand of "natural forest" into what could more aptly be called a tree farm. Their crop cycle was estimated to be thirty years or more. A division of the company was created and dedicated to the managing, cutting, and re-planting of trees. The trees were specifically selected to optimize the production of paper. Their research department sought trees that would grow and mature rapidly. Factors to be considered were growth density, ease of access, growth rate and utility. Was it more beneficial to clear-cut? Or cut selectively?

The Meade paper mill, located on the Escanaba River, processes 2,500 cords of wood and consumes about thirty million gallons of water each day.

A cord of wood is a stack eight feet long, four feet wide and four feet high. In the interest of efficiency the company doesn't actually "measure" the wood that enters the plant gate. They weigh the trucks hauling the pulpwood as they enter and then again as they leave. They convert the weight difference to cords of wood at the rate of two tons per cord. This averages out to be approximately ten cords per truckload. The next time you see a loaded logging truck go by, know that it takes 250 of those loads to provide the 2,500 cords required to keep the Mead Paper Mill operating for one day.

Each cord of wood, for example, can produce 1,200 copies of the National Geographic Magazine - or 900 one-pound books - or 4,000,000 postage stamps - or seven and a half million toothpicks - or 12 dining room tables.

Some trees normally utilized as pulpwood may be selected to satisfy the demand for telephone poles. Those selected as telephone poles could well be shipped as far away as the mountains of Turkey.

Saw logs, more mature trees than those used for pulpwood and large enough to be suitable for lumber, are what furnish building materials. When cut up as lumber the wood is measured and described in board feet. A "board foot" is a piece of lumber one inch thick, one foot long and one foot wide (actually ¼" is subtracted from thickness and width to allow for planing, smoothing the wood). It takes approximately 16,000 board feet (think of one board 1"x12"x3 miles long) to build a 2,000 square foot house. That would equate to 32 cords of wood. Products of the forests are put to many uses.

Bird's eye maples are special trees, maple trees that have been exposed to a disease that permeates the wood without destroying or weakening it. It leaves many small knot-like blemishes that resemble bird's eyes, hence the name. This flaw appears in finished wood as a very unique and attractive pattern. Because of its scarcity and desirability it commands a high price. It can bring as much as $1,000 per marketable log – or more depending on the demand.

Yellow birch, also called curly birch, has a unique and attractive "curly" grain pattern. People who work with wood appreciate these unique forest products for more than their dollar-and-cents value.

You can pick them out by the way they look at the grain, the way they caress it with their hand, the faraway look some get in their eye as they explain how it can be used, how it came to be that way. There's almost a sense of a love affair going on there.

Another lover of things natural it has been my privilege to know lives with his family deep in the woods on Hogsback Mountain just northwest of Marquette. He's a master at finding knots, stumps, and odd shaped pieces, along with choice lumber. He designs and crafts furniture, hand-carves figures and totems, produces one-of-a-kind art work. Another individual who, with his wife, operate a woodworking shop in Big Bay produces specialized furniture and cabinets from forest materials. Trees are a renewable but finite resource. If this resource and us and the corporations who depend on it are all to survive, we must all develop an appreciation for the natural order of all things, the utility of the product and the need for balancing the two. There must be a "feel," a love of wood.

In nature there are no laws – there are only consequences.

♎

The Loggers

Chapel in the Forest

The Prayer

I am the heat of your hearth on a winter night,
Your shade from the summer sun.
My fruits are delicious and refreshing.
The rustle of my leaves is a whispered reassurance.
The sighing of my pine needles is a tranquilizer.
An hour in my forest will restore your soul.
I am the beam of your house, the board of your table,
the handle of your hoe, the door of your homestead.
I am the timber of your ship, the bed on which you lie,
I was the board of your cradle, and will be the shell of your coffin.
I am a tree. Who passes by, take care.
Harm me not.

♎ *unknown*

Photo from Superior View Studios, Marquette, MI

The Farmer

In the early days of farming much of the emphasis was placed on a strong back and hard work – especially as it was applied to a hired hand.

THE HIRED HAND

All societies are carried on the strong backs of the working people. These are the people who get up each day and go to work to provide the delivery of the goods and services on which all of us depend. If you were to ask one of today's children where his or her glass of milk came from the answer they are most apt to give is, "From the grocery store." And, of course, they are right. Next question: Where does the grocery store get the milk? Or the vegetables? Or the ice cream? The answer is probably a blank look. Most have never thought beyond the grocery store. Many of the rest of us don't give it much thought either. The cow is a forgotten contributor.

Some of that milk the child is drinking might have come from cows that live on a farm in Michigan's Upper Peninsula in the township of West Branch. Let me tell you a little about one of the men who worked on that farm.

There's a road in West Branch Township, just a little side road a half mile long or so, that runs east off of county road 545. It's just a little dirt side road. There's a sign at the intersection that gives the road one of those "alphabet" designations that Michigan Counties use. The sign on the corner we're talking about reads "545/TR."

If you were to ask someone in West Branch or the nearby village of Skandia, "Where's road TR?" you'd probably get a puzzled look and, "Road who?" If, on the other hand, you ask, "Where's 'Slippery Jim road?" they'd instantly raise an arm, point in the appropriate direction and say, "Just go west (or east or north or south, depending on where you are). It's a couple hundred feet this (or that) side of the Old Little Lake Road." Then they might look at you closely to see if you indicate any glimmer of understanding. "It runs off east a bit. You can't miss it." Folks who've lived in the area know where "Slippery Jim Road" is - but - how many know anything about "Slippery Jim?"

If you were to be more specific, ask around about Slippery Jim Haslip, you might at first get a blank look, or a squint, a wrinkled brow - you know, that thoughtful look. Then, if the individual was an old timer, they might brighten and reply, "Wasn't he that guy who talked to the radio?" Now that's an answer that ought to peak your curiosity. I'll tell you about that too.

Jim Haslip was one of many wanderers who roamed the country in the nineteen twenties and thirties "lookin' for work." The country was in the grip of the Great Depression. The number one song on the hit parade back then was, "Brother, Can You Spare a Dime?" Everybody was "lookin' for work."

A local family operating a farm in West Branch Township was working hard just to stay even. They had need for "a hired hand." Jim happened along at just the right time.

Jim was of Scottish descent and came to Michigan from Canada. Jim couldn't read nor write but that was not unusual in those days. There were some that said that Jim was – well - the kindest way to put it is that Jim might not count quite as fast as some of the rest of us. This made him easy prey for the boorish among us who seem to delight in making fun of the shortcomings of others. It didn't seem to bother Jim though. Then too he was big enough that no one was apt to push that sort of thing too far. He was a likable fellow, clean, easy going and the kids all seemed to like him. A fella that kids and dogs like can't be a bad guy.

When he "hired on" he was given his own room right in the house with the family. It was just for him and the children knew it as "Jim's room." He had a bed and a chair and kept his few meager belongings in "his room."

Jim was not stupid. He knew about trees, the woods, nature. Sickness on a remote farm back in those days was pretty much a do-it-yourself thing. When someone was sick, especially one of the kids, Jim would go out into the woods and find roots or leaves or pitch from pine tree blisters, something. He'd bring it back and ask "the missus" to put it on an ailing child as a poultice. As often as not it seemed to help. He knew about pruning apple trees too. As I mentioned all the kids seemed to like Jim. The school age children of the household even took it upon themselves to teach Jim reading and writing, at least to the point where Jim could sign his name. No, when the sun finally sets, Jim was not stupid.

One winter night one of the kids was very sick.

Nothing anyone could do seemed to help. She would have to be taken to a doctor. The problem was the nearest doctor was 25 miles away in Marquette and what roads there were were buried in snow. The only hope of getting to town was by train. The railroad track was about two miles away and it was at night. Why is it that when something goes wrong involving children it's always at night?

It was Jim, big Jim who carried that child two miles through the snow and flagged down the train. The child and her momma got to Marquette and the story had a happy ending. Jim walked back home.

When radios first came out they were looked upon as a pretty amazing thing. Suddenly isolated farms could be connected to "the city folks." That box with the knobs and dials that hummed and glowed and spoke to you from distant places told about new and fascinating things. It was miraculous.

Jim thought so too. He reasoned that if someone could speak to him through that thing, why, he ought to be able to talk to them, too. And he did. I would guess that any politicians of that day heard Jim about as well as they hear you and I today. Anyway, no harm was done.

As the economy improved Jim stayed on at that family farm. He was even able to save up a few dollars and he bought a 40-acre plot - you guessed it, you're getting ahead of me - at the end of Slippery Jim Road. He intended to build his own place there but the years were catching up with Jim too. Time passed and his plans never got beyond a few two by fours and good intentions.

Somewhere along the way Jim got the idea that he had once been a State Senator. Maybe it was all that talking on the radio. The men he worked with knew of some of Jim's "peculiarities" and used to humor him. They'd even call him "Senator" at times. He accepted that and took no offense.

As the years passed Jim's mental wanderings began to range pretty far afield. Finally Jim had to be taken to the state mental hospital at Newberry. That's where he lived out the remainder of his allotted time believing he had been a Senator and talking to the radio – just like a real Senator

The sign on that old road off County Road 545 now reads "Slippery Jim Road. I never found out where the "Slippery" in his name came from. Of course if he really had been a senator, talking to the radio, why maybe . . .

Jim, and hundreds like him were a part of building the Upper Peninsula of Michigan. You won't read his name in a history book. There aren't any plaques or pillars erected to his memory but he was part of the memory of this land.

Nobody I ever met or spoke to had a bad thing to say about Jim. We should all live that well.

♎

THE IRON MINERS

Superior View Studios photo, Marquette, MI

Iron Ore Stump

Bill Penglase, an early miner, sits on the stump where iron ore was discovered initiating the Jackson Mine.

Finding the Ore

The white man's migration to Michigan's Upper Peninsula in any great numbers occurred in the mid 1800s. Relations with the Native Americans, many of whom had been pushed here earlier by development further east, was good – or poor – or somewhere in between. Treaties and agreements between the government and the Indians were made and misunderstood and broken. There were a few physical confrontations and some people were killed but life and development moved on. By September of 1844 a government survey team led by surveyor William Austin Burt had reached the shores of Teal Lake near what is now Negaunee in Michigan's Upper Peninsula. Burt noticed that his magnetic compass behaved very erratically. He made note in his log of this peculiarity but was able to continue the survey relying on a device called a "Solar Compass" which he himself had invented.

Word got around about the magnetic compass irregularity Burt had encountered. To some whose interests weren't immersed in the accuracy of a survey the possibility of iron and profits to be made aroused their interest. Philo M. Everret of Jackson, in southern Lower Michigan, organized an interested group of friends and headed north seeking what was being described as a "mountain of iron."

The prospectors landed near the mouth of the Carp River just south of what is present day Marquette. They were accompanied by a guide who professed to know "right where the iron is." That's what he said but "there's many a slip twixt the cup and . . ." and he couldn't find it. Discouraged, the party decided they would continue westward toward the Keweenaw Peninsula thinking they might search for copper. Near the settlement of L'Anse they met Marje Gesick, a Chief of the Teal Lake Band of Ojibwa Indians. When their story of the fruitless search in the Teal Lake area was related the chief told Everret that he knew of that place of iron. It was a special, spiritual place to the Indians. Much lightning struck the earth there. Chief Gesick could take them where that place was.

After some discussion among the members of the party it was decided that they would return with Marje Gesick to search for the iron ore. Back near Teal Lake the Chief led them straight to an overturned pine tree. In the upturned roots they found great chunks of high-grade iron ore. The Jackson Mining Company was created right there on the site with a half share dedicated to Chief Marje Gesick.

In 1847 another group of businessmen from Cleveland became interested the stories of iron ore deposits. This group included Samuel L. Mather. They pooled their resources and formed the Cleveland Iron Mining Company. This was the birth of what would become what we know today as Cleveland Cliffs Incorporated, CCI, "The Company." The Mather group sent men to Michigan's Upper Peninsula to evaluate the stories they were hearing concerning ore deposits and to explore the potential of developing a mine. The advance party found that the iron was indeed there, that it was rich, and that it was readily available. As far as getting it to market - well - that was something else. The rapids of the St. Mary's River where Lake Superior emptied into Lake Huron required a portage.

With a plentiful supply of wood near the ore deposits the developers elected to construct forges near the mining sites. The forges were to reduce the bulk of the high-grade ore found on the surface to a higher iron concentrate called bloom iron. The initial delivery of a test case of bloom iron from the mine/forge site to Cleveland, Ohio, incurred costs estimated at $200 per ton. The market price of iron at that time was $85 per ton. There had to be a better way.

The initial development of this mining in a far northern wilderness required that laborers, men be attracted to the area. Not only was the location remote but Americans of that day were not attracted to this hard, dirty work. In addition living conditions in this developing land were primitive at best.

The workers the mining companies were able to recruit were mainly immigrants. To keep them they also had to furnish living accommodations, housing, food, clothing, all this had to be provided. A few hardy wives accompanied their men to this frontier. These family groups often ran boarding houses to serve the needs of single or unaccompanied workers. The "Company Store" was a creation to supply the bare necessities to workers and families. These austere living conditions forged a socio-economic relationship between the workers and the company. It was a relationship similar to a feudal system, very much like the southern plantation system. There were supervisors, management lived in "the big house" while the workers lived in company houses not unlike "slave row." It was slavery with a forced paternalism.

Miners daily pounded, blasted, and shoveled the rich ore out of rock-faced surface outcrops. Wheelbarrows and two-wheel horse carts transported it to larger carriages or iron forges. Horse drawn carriages also hauled the ore or the bloom iron to the loading dock at Marquette.

At the dock more men with wheelbarrows would trundle the ore into the holds of wooden ships. Early operations at all levels were highly dependent on the muscle power of men and animals. Competition among the several mining companies that had sprung up led to mergers and combinations. Smaller companies were absorbed by larger companies - or forced out.

The need for charcoal to fuel the forges created a subsidiary forestry industry. This need was filled by individuals who preferred woods work to mining or by the mining companies forming a wood cutting division. Visionaries of that day imagined the area becoming a "Pittsburgh of the Midwest."

Transporting ore and bloom iron from the

mines and forges to the dock at Marquette presented its own set of problems. The land rose approximately 900 feet over a distance of about ten miles. Maintenance of the roadway in the range of weather experienced was a continuing problem. With a common problem the various companies cooperated in the construction of a plank road. Everything that came or went traveled by ship. Mules and horses, necessary to pull the carts and wagons, were in high demand and short supply. Even with the improved plank road heavy carriages of iron moving downhill were difficult to control. The animal's footing on the plank roads was poor, especially when the planks were wet. Braking systems for the carriages was equally poor. Accidents were frequent.

In an effort to improve control wooden "rails" capped with iron straps were laid on the planks. The carriage wheels were made to fit the rails. In spite of these improvements the inefficiency of braking systems coupled with poor footing for the animals made control precarious. Accidents, often fatal to men, mules, and horses, seemed an unavoidable part of the job.

♎

The Iron Miners

Superior View Studios photo, Marquette, MI

Jackson Mine

The mine-face of the Jackson mine. Men worked 12 hour shifts using primitive tools and mining methods.

The Early Years

Docking facilities for loading ships were built in Marquette. Then Lake Superior, one evening shortly after construction was completed, washed the whole thing away overnight. The dock was rebuilt and a portion of breakwater was added to mitigate the force of the waves.

Wooden sailing ships were the only means of shipping the raw ore in these early days. A dock was necessary for loading. With the ship tied up to the dock ore would be loaded by men filling, pushing and dumping wheelbarrows. The loading rate was about 50 tons per day. Once the ship reached Sault Ste. Marie at the east end of Lake Superior the rapids of the St. Mary's River presented an obstacle. The ore then had to be off-loaded, carted around the rapids, and reloaded on a second ship below the rapids. This labor-intensive delay added considerably to the cost of transportation and represented a major bottleneck to the flow of material.

In 1855, in response to this problem at the Soo, Charles T. Harvey, who had been a salesman for a scale company, supervised the construction of a lock that would allow ships to bypass the St. Mary's Rapids. Upon completion of the lock ships could be raised to enter Lake Superior or lowered to continue down the St. Mary's River avoiding the costly portaging. The first year the lock was in operation 1,450 tons of iron ore passed through it.

Shipping costs of the ore from the mines to Marquette were now three dollars per ton: from Marquette to the ports on Lake Erie was an additional five dollars per ton. With this drastic decrease in transportation costs the economic incentive to operate forges at the mines disappeared.

Among Great Lakes ship captains iron ore was not a favored cargo. It was bulky, it was dirty and it stained their decks red. It soon became apparent to all concerned however that the shipping of iron ore was the future of transportation on the Great Lakes. Ships were now being designed and built specifically for hauling ore. Marine companies were formed to meet the growing demand for boats. Upper Michigan's Marquette Range iron ore was now able to reach the steel mills at competitive prices.

The safety problems involved in moving the ore from the mines to the docks at Marquette continued. It remained a hair-raising, gut-twisting and costly operation damaging equipment and injuring and killing men and animals. In 1857 another attempt to solve this problem was tried. A railroad was built. Iron tracks were laid from the docks to the mines. A powerful steam engine pulling larger carriages took the place of the horses and oxen. The braking system of these heavy trains was much more efficient than that of the wagons had been. The accident rate plummeted immediately. Ore could now be moved quicker, more safely and in greater quantity.

Eighteen fifty-eight saw an additional improvement. This change involved loading procedures at the dock. The dock itself was elevated,

built higher than the decks of the ships. "Pocket" compartments were built into the docks directly below the tracks. The ore could more easily and quickly be emptied from the ore cars into these pockets. When a ship was brought alongside the dock a retractable chute mounted adjacent to the pocket on the outside of the dock could be lowered to the ship's open hatch. A door on the bottom of the pocket could be opened and the ore would slide down the chute, through the open hatch and directly into the ship's hold. Although this method of loading was more efficient than the wheelbarrow system, "trimmers," men with shovels, had to be sent down into the ship's hold. These "trimmers" manually shoveled ore from one side of the ship to the other to keep the ship "in trim."
Steam powered tugboats were also being introduced to the lakes trade eliminating a shipper's dependence on the fickle winds to power the ships and meet schedules. The steam tugs would tow one or more of the sailing ships transforming them into cargo barges. Transit time was reduced and schedules were much more predictable.

These combined improvements further reduced shipping cost to $.87 per ton from the mines to Marquette and $2.09 per ton from Marquette to ports on Lake Erie.

Back at the mines the consolidation of various mining companies was further increasing ore production and efficiency. The Cleveland Company purchased the Marquette Iron Company, created by Amos Harlow and Robert Gravaraet. "The Company," the organization that would one day be Cleveland Cliffs Incorporated, was taking shape.

In 1857 a nonmine associated complication arose. A financial panic swept the country. The circulation of money in the country's economic system was severely curtailed. William Ferguson, the mining agent for The Cleveland Company at Marquette, was able to persuade his workmen to continue working and wait for their pay. With this lack of United State's currency in circulation, W. J. Gordon, also an employee of the mining company, instituted what came to be called "Iron Money." This was paper money the company itself printed, circulated and it was used as cash. With this Iron Money widely accepted families could pay their rent, their utility bills, purchase groceries and clothing, whatever they needed. These purchases were all transacted through the company and at the company store. It would be many months before the financial crisis would be over and Iron Money could be redeemed for federal currency.

Samuel L. Mather, representing The Cleveland Company, traveled to the banks in New York and Boston searching for necessary financing. In addition to the assets of the Cleveland Company and the sterling record of the company itself, it was the strength of Samuel Mather's personal integrity that enabled the company to borrow the necessary cash. He had succeeded in obtaining further financing but the question remained: would it be enough? The Marquette Range alone was facing the immediate need for $50,000.

There was a close dependency between employees and employers in those early days. The relationship however was heavily weighted on the side of the employer. The social situation closely resembled slavery with the employer in control of all aspects of the employee's welfare. The mines and their neighboring communities in these early days were very isolated. The Northern Upper Michigan area was still pretty much a wilderness. Even those residents who were self-employed, those working in occupations peripheral to the mining operations, were indirectly dependent on the company and dependent on the company store for provisions

Mining in these early days was a surface operation. Work crews were comprised mainly of young, strong, unskilled immigrants. Many were already in the work force as young as twelve years old. A shift was ten hours long and the men worked six days a week. The pay scale was about a dollar a day.

One hard working Italian immigrant managed to set aside enough from his meager pay to send to Italy for his wife and their two sons. With him and his two sons working, saving as much as they could, he was finally able to send for his four daughters.

Another woman, with the help of her children - everyone was expected to work back then – not only kept house for her husband and their seven children but also took in thirteen boarders. Room and board arrangements included cleaning the rooms, making the beds, cooking and serving meals, packing the miner's lunches, and doing everybody's laundry. These were the days before vacuum cleaners, washing machines, and electric ovens. It was brooms, scrub-boards and wood stoves. It was all done by hand - and these were considered good times.

By 1865 the rich surface ore was pretty much gone. To follow the ore veins miners were digging tunnels to follow a known vein or simply exploring.

By 1877 a hollow diamond-tipped drill bit had been developed for exploring. This bit could be driven into the ground and recovered. The hollow drill would contain a cross section sample of the strata below. It was extremely useful for locating new veins of underground ore. Engineers were able to drill in several locations to find and chart the ore strata.

In 1880 the first of many underground mine shafts was sunk. Some shafts would eventually be 5,000 feet deep. Steam furnished the power to operate hoists for raising and lowering men and for lifting waste and ore. Steam power was also necessary to power water pumps to keep the mineshafts from flooding.

In this strange underground world the only light would come from a candle. Two phenomenon immediately became apparent: a single candle can produce a surprising amount of light, and, secondly, you have never experienced "dark" until you've been underground and that candle goes out.

♎

The Iron Miners

File Photo, Peter White Public Library, Marquette, MI

William G. Mather

"Noblesse Oblige"

By 1867 the Cleveland Iron Company, "The Company," had entered the shipping business. They purchased half interest in the wooden ore carrier "George Sherman." The company's intent in entering the shipping business was an attempt to acquire control of all subsidiary operations that would affect their ability to mine and market iron ore. By 1888 the first of the steel-hulled steamships appeared on the lakes. Shipping was a facet of the business the company would remain involved in for many years.

By 1890 competition and market pressures had whittled the mining operations down to two major companies; Cleveland Iron Company headed by Samuel L. Mather and the Iron Cliffs Company headed by Samuel J. Tilden. Discussions were entered into exploring the possible merger of these two companies. Unfortunately Samuel L. Mather would not live to see the completion.

His son, William G. Mather, a graduate of Trinity College of Hartford, Connecticut, had begun working for the company in 1878 in the position of clerk, to "learn the business" from the ground up. He quickly rose through the hierarchy to the position of Vice President. With his father's death he succeeded to head of the company. The in-progress merger with

Iron Cliffs Company was carried out successfully and the merger was completed by 1891. The Cleveland Cliffs Iron Company had been formed. With this consolidation behind them the drive to develop new technologies, to do things faster, better and with less expense continued.

In 1890, foreshadowing things to come in the future, an attempt had been made at "ore benefaction," an attempt to raise the iron content of the ore by crushing and washing. This early experiment proved to be unsuccessful, however advances in other areas were being made. Electric locomotives were introduced for below ground work in 1892. This replaced horses and eased the load on human muscle considerably.

Among the men who worked the mines immigrants made up the majority of the labor force. They came mainly from Europe and the Scandinavian countries and, of course, brought their character, customs and language with them. It seems a natural human trait to be wary of strangers, especially if the stranger doesn't speak your language. These various ethnic groups tended to draw together, to limit their association to those who shared their language and customs. As time went by recognition of the common problems and shared hardships of these workers began to erode these ethnic barriers.

A panic in the nation's financial markets in 1893 led to layoffs and pay reductions in the mines.

In 1892 the mines in the Marquette Range had been employing 17,000 men. With the panic of '93 that count dropped to 3,500. The pay scale for those workers remaining had also fallen - to $12. Not $12 per hour - not even $12 per week. The pay scale was $12 per month! And that was for 10 hour days six days a week. That pay scale figured out to be between four and five cents an hour - with no fringe benefits or unemployment insurance or welfare, not even very much sympathy.

These shared hardships and severe conditions drew the workers together, bonding them in spite of their ethnic differences. On July 13, 1895, the miners walked out together over a dispute concerning a ten-cent pay increase for each car of ore raised - and for recognition of their fledgling union. The company countered their demands with a pay raise but refused to recognize their union. As the dispute dragged on no one was working. No one was tending to the water pumps down in the mining shafts. With the pumps shut down the mines were beginning to flood. Both sides of the dispute were experiencing pressure to get the problem settled.

In these early days transportation, especially from a way up in the wilds of Northern Michigan, was primitive to nonexistent. The workmen had arrived on the iron range without much more than the clothes on their backs – and many of them brought families with them. The miners were dependent on the company for housing, for food, for utilities and all the necessities of life. The company owned the store and the utilities. For medical emergencies, the men were dependent on the company's medical staff. It was the way of life in the early days to rent a company-owned house and to have an account at the company store. The expenses would be deducted from a man's monthly pay – which more often than not left very little of that $12.00 per month. Some families never seemed to get out of debt month after month with the breadwinner working a full shift.

Compare this to the lot of a slave on a southern plantation: African slaves were brought to the United States in the holds of ships. These migrants, most of them, came over "in steerage," in the hold of a ship. The slaves worked for their owners, lived in quarters provided by the owner, and ate and wore what the owner provided. These immigrant miners worked for - - and lived - - - and, well, at least the miners didn't have leg irons and whips to contend with.

The idea of banding together, to speak with one voice, to unite was a groundbreaking idea. Management, of course, was not in favor of this move. The company believed it was a radical idea and dangerous. It smacked of socialism, men banding together to achieve a common goal. In later years, when the term gained greater notoriety, it would be broad-brush branded Communism, called un-American.

With the standoff and the mineshafts beginning to flood William G. Mather, as Company President, made a trip to Ishpeming. The company also called in the Michigan State Militia to "maintain order and prevent violence and property damage." To stop the flooding problem Mather brought in outside workers. With the militia maintaining order and the threat of flooding contained the major reasons for the company to settle the dispute were eliminated. The walkout finally ended September 20, two months and one week after it had begun. Any further attempts at union formation anywhere in the Upper Peninsula ended.

To William Mather, who remained a bachelor 'til the age of 72, the company and its people were his life - his family. He was not unaware of the hardships experienced by the miners. He also realized that the morale and welfare of the workers and their families was an important factor to the overall success of the company operation. He believed this so strongly that in 1898, at a joint meeting of the Lake Superior Mining Institute, he voiced his feelings in what was considered a revolutionary recommendation. In later years it would come to be called the Magna Carta of mining, the first recognition of the rights of the working miners.

In his speech he pointed out that labor represented 70% of the total operating cost of the mine. Men - good men – he said, should not be hired, let go, and then expected to wait around to be hired again. There was a need to offer job security. Further there was a need to provide good housing and low rents. There was a need for help for the workers to build their own homes, for proper sanitation, to have garden plots and flower gardens. There should be schools for the children. There should be welfare programs to aid families in need. A pension plan was needed to provide security for older workers. Safety should be promoted. Provisions should be made for family medical care. Those workers who were injured and the families of the men who had been killed should be provided for. He ended his speech with these remarks:

> *"I would not like to close, however, without bearing witness to the feeling that upon us who have been more favored by education and opportunity, there rests that obligation so well expressed by the words 'noblesse oblige'."*

("'Noblesse oblige'." A French expression meaning those of high birth, wealth, or social position must behave generously or nobly toward others: literally, 'nobility obligates'.")

In following their president's philosophy the Cleveland Cliffs Iron Company initiated a program to provide a payment of one dollar per day to any man disabled by an accident. A widow would receive a $200 death benefit. An assessment of 25 cents per month would be taken from each man's pay - a sum to be matched by the company - to pay for these benefits. An additional assessment of one dollar per month would provide medical care for each man and his family. Workers would henceforth have a representative on the mine's policy-making board to assure that their interests would be represented.

These were revolutionary ideas for their time. These would prove to be the first tentative steps, the beginnings of a movement away from the wasteful dictatorial antagonism that existed between labor and management and toward a mutually beneficial program of cooperation and consideration

The Iron Miners

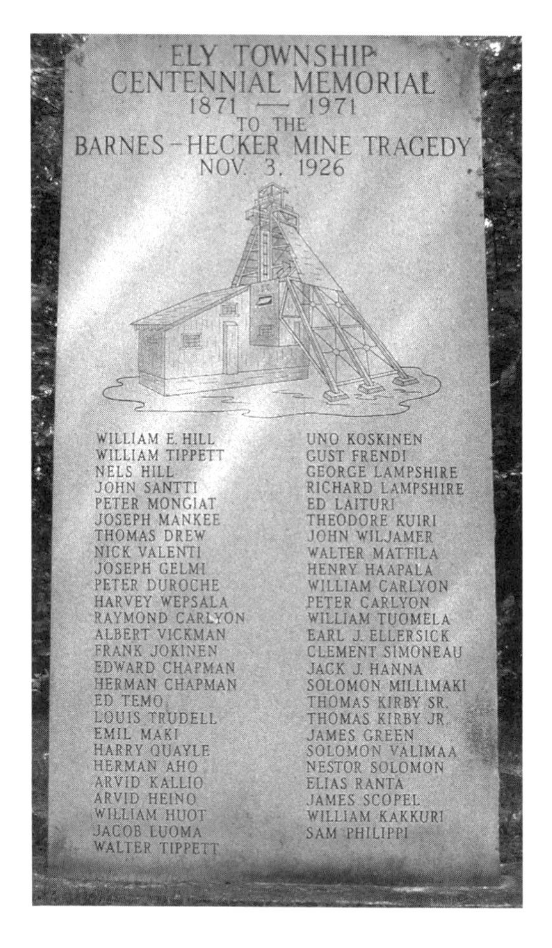

Barnes Hecker Monument

In memory of those men who lost their lives in the Barnes Hecker mine disaster. It stands on the grounds of the Michigan Iron Industry Museum.

Disaster!

The early twentieth century saw Cleveland Cliffs expand into the Mesabi Range in Minnesota. Mesabi ore was a poorer grade than in the Marquette area but it was easier to mine. There were also tax advantages so the company elected to retain the majority of its operations in Michigan.

In administrative moves that further validated William G. Mather's concerns for the workers the company enacted more of his 1898 recommendations. In 1905 they established an employee welfare department within the company. In 1911 they initiated a safety department with a full time engineer to recommend and implement safer work practices. The implementation of the safety considerations resulted in an almost immediate fifty percent reduction of the accident rate. These policies of concern for the worker couldn't help but increase the morale and efficiency of the entire operation.

In 1918 Bell Memorial Hospital was built in Ishpeming. It was to provide medical care for company employees and their families. Many residents of the area today took their first breath in that hospital.

Expanding these programs even further the

company initiated night school classes, called "Cliffs Americanization Project," in an effort to teach immigrant workers basic English. This concern wasn't entirely philanthropic either. A work force wherein everyone understood the same language would further increase safety, efficiency and productivity. It also enabled many immigrant workers to pass the required naturalization examinations, to become United States Citizens.

In further official recognition of the benefits achieved by the introduction of President Mather's paternalistic views the company introduced the landscaping of the company grounds. They also encouraged the implementation of this program to the worker's homes. Their belief was that beautiful surroundings would promote pride, pride of the men in themselves and in the company. A landscaping awards program was initiated in which prizes were awarded to families with the neatest and best-maintained homes and gardens. Living standards and worker morale also increased.

President Mather went so far as to commission landscape architect Warren Manning to design a town that he envisioned as a model for housing workers. The town would be named "Gwinn" in honor of Mather's mother, Elizabeth Gwinn Mather. In this new village the company would subsidize the price of the lots, the homes and building materials for employees. The town was built in accordance with his directions and many older residents still refer to the village of Gwinn, Michigan, as "Model Town."

In 1910 the increasing need for electrical power to operate the mines and provide for housing led the company to construct their first hydroelectric dam and power plant. It was located on the Autrain River. As the need for power continued to grow the company would invest in more dams and power generating stations.

In 1912, to satisfy demand and to handle increased mine production, a modern steel "Pocket Dock," was built near Presque Isle in Marquette. Winter ice has always been a limiting factor of the time the boats could operate on Lake Superior. This modern pocket dock provides a faster, more efficient means of transferring ore. This decreases turn-around time when loading boats and maximizes their utility during the shipping season. All these improvements paid for themselves in efficiency and added to the company's profit margin. That Presque Isle dock continues in operation and is the only active loading facility remaining in Marquette.

With the development of Coast Guard ice breaking ships, the field ice, which once closed the lakes to shipping, could be overcome and the shipping season extended. The winter shipping problem now became flow ice at the locks in Sault Ste Marie. This broken up flow ice tends to enter the lock ahead of the boat filling all or part of the lock. There was insufficient room remaining for the boat. Passing ships through the locks in these conditions was not economically feasible.

On November 3, 1926, a tragedy struck the Marquette Iron Range. At 11:20 in the morning underground miners were blasting a new cut below ground at the Barnes-Hecker mine. Following the detonation of one of the blasts one of the miners, Wilfred Wills, sensed that something was wrong.

Survival in a mine often depends on staying alert and responding rapidly when senses indicate things are not right. Wills first heard a strange muffled roaring noise. He sensed an increase in the air pressure on his eardrums. He immediately left the drift where he was working and ran toward the main shaft. The main shaft was the way out of the mine. When he arrived the cage, the elevator for raising and lowering the men, was not there. He signaled repeatedly for the operator to send it down but received no response.

Unknown to Wills at the time water was rapidly filling the mine. It had reached the machinery at a lower level of the main shaft. Electrical wiring had been short-circuited. The motor operating the lift was not functioning. With the drive motor dead the lift was no longer operational.

Several other miners, sensing that all was not well had also gathered at the lift station. "Climb the shaft ladder!" Wills shouted. The men began scrambling frantically up the ladder toward the surface. Wills was in the lead.

Unseen behind them a mass of black water was surging into and rapidly filling the main shaft. The water level rose rapidly toward the struggling men. One by one the dark water overtook the franticly struggling miners. The man immediately behind Wills lost his hold and disappeared into the swirling flood.

Of the 52 men who descended those 52 steps from the dry house that morning, rode the cage down the main shaft to work, only one man made it to the surface. Wilfred Wills was the sole survivor.

When word of the Barnes-Hecker disaster reached William Mather he responded immediately with more than sympathy and oratory. He ordered that the widows of the disaster victims receive double the normal death benefit compensation. He also ordered that there be no further costs to these families for house rent, for electricity, for water or for any company provided utilities.

The sons of the victims of this disaster, when they reached the age of eighteen, would have a job waiting for them at CCI, guaranteed, if they wanted it. This caring and compassionate attitude was a further example of the character of this company president and his paternalistic attitude toward "his" company. This prompt and compassionate action further bonded employee loyalty to the company, his company.

These were the attitudes, the policies he had attempted to convince his fellow executives to implement in his speech of 1898. It was also the tentative beginning of labor management relations as they would develop between the United Steel Workers of America and Cleveland Cliffs Incorporated.

Efforts to recover the bodies of the men lost had to be abandoned. The Barnes Hecker subterranean strata was very unstable. It was further complicated by the added hazards caused by the massive flooding. The Barnes-Hecker mine was closed and sealed, never to be re-opened. A memorial to the men who had lost their lives was erected on the site. The marker has since been moved to stand at the Michigan Iron Industry Museum located between Negaunee and Marquette.

In 1929 an economic tragedy struck not only the mining community but the nation as a whole. In October of that year the stock market collapsed, crashed! Hard times soon stalked the land. Depressed economic conditions drove Cleveland Cliffs, along with many other companies, to the verge of bankruptcy.

Company President Mather, in what many have called his finest hour, put up his personal fortune alongside the faith and credit of the company to obtain sorely needed financing. In the face of the nation's crumbling economy and national ruin people looked for jobs that no longer existed. William Mather was concerned not with personal security but with the survival of the company. He was searching for a means whereby the company and those who depended on it could continue to exist. Chief Executives of the caliber of William G. Mather, managing "his" company with a philosophy of "Noblesse Oblige" are an exceedingly rare and precious commodity.

By 1945 the effects of World War II had buoyed the iron ore industry. The need for steel to construct war materials in the United States, the "Arsenal of Democracy," resurrected the sagging economy. The crisis that began with the stock market crash of 1929 had ended.

In the 1940s labor again attempted to organize. With the advent of World War II a patriotic fervor swept the country and active union organization was put on hold for the duration. It is interesting to speculate whether or not the attitudes created by President Mather's past actions didn't contribute to the united efforts of labor and management.

Following the successful outcome of World War II the attempt to organize labor again arose. By this time the movement had spread across the country and was achieving wide success. Resistance from owners was as strong as ever but labor was now in demand. The supply of laborers was limited. It was not as easy as it had been "in the old days" to find replacement workers. The Union organizers said management was "unfair" – and sometimes it was.

Management spread rumors that the Unions were "Communists" - and some of them were

In 1946, Joe Pascoe and Jack Powell were instrumental in bringing the United Steel Workers of America to the mines of Upper Michigan. It wasn't an easy task but the time had come for change. It was long overdue that the miners represent themselves as a united group.

Almost as if acknowledging these changing social conditions William G. Mather, at the age of 90, stepped down as the leader of CCI. Between he and his father, Samuel Mather, they had imprinted over 100 years of the Mather family character and enlightened guidance upon Cleveland Cliffs Incorporated. An era had come to an end. Edward Greene was named to succeed Mather. Mather was kept on the board in what today would be called a consulting role.

In 1951, at the age of 94, William G. Mather died. Seventy-eight years of "Noblesse Oblige" had ended.

The Iron Miners

Photo courtesy United Steel Workers of America, local 7798

Ernie Ronn

A Miner's Miner

"Come on in. Would you like a cup of Coffee?" That was the greeting as I walked up to the door of Ernie and Beatrice (Juntinen) Ronn's beautiful home on the bank of the Autrain River. It brought back memories. It was a greeting that hearkened back to a time gone by. But I was here to see and talk with Ernie Ronn about another time gone by so I guess I shouldn't have been surprised.

Ernie is a couple years my senior and has roots buried deep in Marquette Range Iron Ore. That ore deposit, discovered back in the 1840s, and the immigrant workers who were brought in to exploit it are what made this land. And they're what shaped Ernie and Beatrice Ronn too. There are few monuments to these simple folks who poured their hearts and souls into the mining of iron ore to build our nation. In the process they were searching for a better life. It may have been the vision and the risk of capital that allowed the exploitation of these resources but it was the men, the men who wielded the picks, shoveled the ore, and pushed the wheelbarrow that brought it about. As Ernie is fond of saying, "Those men may have recited the Lord's prayer many times and in many languages but they never said '. . . GIVE us this day our daily bread . . .' their prayer was 'Let us earn our daily bread.'"

I better tell you a little about Ernie, so you can better understand where he's coming from. Ernie was born in the Bell Memorial Hospital on June 15, 1925.

He got his first smack on the butt from a Cleveland Cliffs doctor. He grew up on Ann Street in Negaunee graduating from the Negaunee High School on the 13th of June 1943. Since he lived just a couple hundred feet from where his father worked in the Negaunee Mine he quickly learned a couple of facts that weren't taught in school: When the sheaves on the hoist house weren't turning, Santa Claus wasn't apt to come around. And when the sheaves weren't turning the teamster who delivered groceries was pretty scarce too.

He started work in the Negaunee Mine, midnight shift, nine days after graduation. He was following a family tradition. His father worked in the mine, his grandfather, his uncles, actually Ernie's family represents over 400 years spent working in the mines.

World War II had come along and Ernie was classified 1A. Uncle Sam's Army had need of his services. After two years and service in the 101st Airborne Division Ernie returned to Negaunee - and to a miner's helmet, a carbide lamp and the mine.

A Union for the workmen was being organized about then and the efforts were anything but smooth. There were some members of management who looked only at the bottom line of the profit and loss statement. To them the workmen were no more than a cost of production. They were materials to be purchased at as low a price as possible. They were tools to be used in the same way as shovels and picks. If they broke or wore out, they would be replaced.

Union organizers attempted to recruit the men, to surmount their ethnic differences, to get them to band together and form a union. The company sent individuals to determine who the organizers were, to identify "troublemakers" and keep them from stirring up trouble. It all came to a head on February 8,1946. At midnight the miners walked out. Their first strike was on.

The company looked for incidents to justify calling in the National Guard as had happened before up in Keweenaw. The miners tried hard and kept their cool. The company thought the strike might be broken if local businesses cut off credit to the strikers. One small shopkeeper stated the situation very clearly. With evidence of his immigrant background still heavy in his speech he stood up at that meeting and asked when the last time (the anti-strike speaker) had been in his shop? In the silence that followed he said in his broken English, "If I have one loaf of bread in my shop, my family will get half and the miners get half. We will starve together!"

These were the people Ernie and Beatrice Ronn grew up with. These were the people who lived along Ann Street – and throughout Negaunee and

Ishpeming. Nobody locked their doors in those neighborhoods. Nobody had to. Their word could be "taken to the bank." If they said they'd do something, they did it. And if you stopped by to visit, they said, "Come on in. Would you like a cup of coffee?" (If they had a cup of coffee to offer.)

Ernie continued working in the mines. He joined the Union, became a member of the Union grievance committee and later President of the Local. The United Steel Workers of America recognized his enthusiasm and ability and hired him first as a Staff Representative and later as Safety Coordinator. The Federal Government also took notice of this champion of the miner's cause and appointed him to the Federal Mine Safety Advisory Board where his duties had him traveling nationwide. He was soon Chairman of that group and was often called upon to represent the labor relations and safety considerations of the United States Government to members of visiting foreign labor groups.

After a lifetime mining Ernie has retired and written a book, "52 Steps Underground, the autobiography of a miner." If you wonder about the life of an iron miner, humor and hardship, "with the bark on," pick up a copy of Ernie's book. Walk those "52 steps," 52 steps that lead to a cable-run man-car. It's a ride that'll take you down, down where "it's as dark as a dungeon way down in the mine."

♎

The Iron Miners

Time to Celebrate

In 1997 Cleveland Cliffs Incorporated sponsored a 150 year celebration of its mining on the Marquette Range. Current and past employees and their families all attended. All enjoyed a good time

Here and Now

The high-grade ore for which the Marquette Range was famous was nearly depleted. Steel from foreign mills, modernized to a higher level of efficiency by US foreign aid following World War II, was soon finding its way onto US markets at competitive prices. To meet this competition in 1950 Cleveland Cliffs opened a research laboratory near the mines in Ishpeming, Michigan.

Working with the US Bureau of Mines, this newly established laboratory was instrumental in developing a means of concentrating low-grade ore into a richer, higher iron content product. This new method was called "pelletizing." Crushing the mined raw ore on site, mixing it with a water-based slurry, and separating the high-grade ore from the slag waste magnetically or through sedimentation did it. The first pellets, they were solid balls approximately the size of the end of a person's thumb, were produced at Eagle Mills in 1956. Poorer grade ore bodies could once more be mined, concentrated on-site and shipped to help American steel companies to be competitive in the existing market.

"Open pit" mining was once more possible and, with the birth of pelletizing, produced a competitive product. The Empire mine was opened in 1963. The neighboring Tilden mine followed in 1974. The last of the underground mines, The Mather "B," was shut down in 1979.

Away from active mines, the lore and history of mining's past had found a champion in a local "old timer," a man named Frank Mathews.

Frank had collected tools, pictures, memorabilia, and single handedly created a one-man iron-mining museum. His lonely efforts finally received the recognition it deserved from the Michigan Historical Center at the State Capital in Lansing.

In 1987 the Michigan Iron Industry Museum was erected on a parcel of land near the Carp River Forge, the site where the first iron bloom had been made a hundred years ago. Although Frank Mathews has died, many of his artifacts have joined the continuing story of iron mining and are now housed in that museum. The Michigan Iron Industry Museum isn't any easier to find than was the area's first iron but it's well worth the effort. Watch for the signs.

In 1981 the Republic Mine whose ore quality once set the industry standard was closed. The closure was first thought to be a temporary measure but in 1996 the closure was made permanent.

In 1985 the name of the company was changed from Cleveland Cliffs Iron Company to Cleveland Cliffs Incorporated. The Cleveland Cliffs Iron Company now became a subsidiary of this parent corporation that included several steel companies. In 1986 the corporation also acquired Pickands, Mather & Co. In 1996 CCI expanded its operations entering into a joint venture to produce high quality iron briquettes in Trinidad.

The company over the years has divested itself of many of its peripheral operations: a forest products division; their interests in charcoal and wood products; the marine division, their electrical generating plants. They have chosen to concentrate on mining, refining and marketing iron ore. They are the world's largest producer of iron ore pellets and the leading supplier of high-quality iron ore products to the steel industry of North America.

The growth and increased efficiency of Cleveland Cliffs and the iron ore industry has been phenomenal. Looking back 150 years it took a crew of men with wheelbarrows six days to load 300 tons of ore aboard a ship. Modern pocket docks now load 12,000 tons in 16 minutes. The "Columbia," the first ore carrier through the Soo locks, carried 120 tons of raw ore. Modern 1,000 foot steel-hulled freighters can carry over 63,000 tons of concentrated pellets. All this efficiency enabled CCI to report net income of $61 million in 1996. North American iron ore pellet sales were a record 11 million tons, proof of the validity of the admonition of William G. Mather - never sell the ore reserves.

As a part of the 1997 150 year Sesquicentennial Celebration, then Chairman and Chief Executive Officer M. Thomas Moore announced "Legacy Grants" to the these local Upper Peninsula of Michigan agencies:

- $150,000 to the National Ice Center at Northern Michigan University.
- $50,000 to the US Ski Hall of Fame & Museum

in Ishpeming.

- $100,000 to the City of Ishpeming for Suicide Hill Ski & Recreation Area.
- $20,000 toward the renovation and repair of the Negaunee Ice Arena
- $100,000 toward the expansion of the Peter White Public Library expansion.

They also indicated they, CCI, will support a memorial project for the village of Republic and the now closed Republic Mine.

A "picnic" was sponsored by the corporation, held in Marquette's Superior Dome for the enjoyment of employees and former employees of "The Company," of CCI. Popular musical groups from times gone by were located and brought in to stir the memories of the old-timers. There were games for the kids. Food was catered from Northern Michigan University's kitchens totaling 105 cases of chicken, 100 cases of brats, 90 cases of hot dogs, 10 cases of baked beans including all the trimmings and selections of deserts. Soft drinks and 60 kegs of beer (some things never change) were consumed.

Groups everywhere were discussing "The old days" - "when the men were made of iron and the ships were made of wood." "You young fella's (and don't overlook the ladies) will never know what it was like to - etc. etc. etc."

Had William G. Mather been there he would

have been proud.

♎

Jack Anderson photo

The "Peter A"

The "Peter A," a 56 foot diesel-powered fishing boat designed and built in 1932. It was named for the company's founder, the Anderson boy's father

FISHERMEN - & WOMEN

Picture this. It's late fall in the Upper Peninsula of Michigan. You're standing on the shore looking out across Lake Superior, the Great Inland Sea. The thermometer reads 30 degrees. Snow is coming down, tiny ice pellets driven hard before a northwest wind. It's a wind that goes right through you. The great gray waves of the big lake roll in steadily, relentlessly, snarling occasionally, showing their teeth. They attack the jagged shoreline crashing against stone that has been there since forever. White spray arches high in the air, pauses momentarily, motionless, and then collapses escaping back into the lake from whence it came. It's the kind of weather a person prefers to watch through a window from a warm room. Some wag might comment, "'I'd sure hate to be out there in a row boat."

Back in the late 1800s, when the city of Marquette was just a wilderness outpost, when miners up the road in Ishpeming, Negaunee, the Keweenaw Peninsula were toiling ten-hour days six days a week for ten dollars, there were people "out there in a rowboat." They toiled ten, twelve even more hour days on that cold and heartless inland sea. They were fishermen - and women – making their living lifting nets, catching herring and lake trout and whitefish.

One pair of those "fishermen" was a couple, Peter Anderson and his wife Anna. Peter and Anna had emigrated from Sweden. They first went to Kansas City and later to Chicago where they lived through the Great Chicago Fire of October, 1871. They moved on to Marquette in 1872. Using the skills common on the coast of their native Sweden they began fishing.

They fished from a small open boat. They would sail when the wind was fair, row when it wasn't. The season began as soon as they could get out through the ice to set their nets. It ended when the ice returned locking them in port.

There was urgency to fishing in those days. The icy grip of winter was close behind that north wind. Once the harbor froze there would be no more fishing, no more income. There was no "unemployment compensation" in those days either. The choice was simple: You make it – or not.

As their three sons, John and Albert and Henry, grew and were able to help the Andersons bought a larger boat, a two-masted 30-foot sailboat with a single cylinder auxiliary gasoline engine. The sons accompanied their father fishing while their mother, Anna, and the daughters, Ann and Caroline, stayed ashore. The women would make and mend and boil the nets while the men were at sea. Everybody worked.

During the winter the boys got jobs at Johnson Fisheries in Chicago. They learned new skills such as the craft of filleting and boning fish for the market. They also learned more about the business of the sale and marketing of fish. They saw a ready market for fresh fish, Anderson Company fish available in Chicago.

The Anderson Fish Company quickly arranged their schedules to match the timetable of the Marquette-to-Chicago train. The train would, on occasion, delay its departure 'til the Anderson shipment of fish arrived to serve the market in Chicago.

Negotiating a loan of $5,000 (a gigantic sum in 1895) the Andersons built a fish house at the foot of Main Street in Marquette. In 1899 they purchased the "Columbia," an 86-foot steam-driven passenger liner out of Escanaba converting it to operate as a fishing boat. With this larger steam-powered boat they were able to expand the area of their fishing grounds. They made frequent trips from Marquette to points as far away as Duluth, Minnesota.

They would set their nets in spots they had selected through trial and error, dead reckoning, and the use of a hand held "lead line." By trial and error they located underwater reefs that were rich with fish.

"Dead reckoning" was the accepted method of navigation in those days: go straight north at six miles per hour for two hours and the boat would be 12 miles north of – the starting point. Change the heading; run further, check the time, and estimate where you were. They knew when the engine was "turning revolutions" to attain six miles per hour because a rudder control line would set up a sympathetic harmonic vibration.

A "lead line," a lead weight attached to a line calibrated in "fathoms," six-foot lengths, would be cast over the side. When it struck the bottom, the calibrations, usually small knots tied in the line, were counted to determine the depth of the water.

Determining the depth of the water helped confirm or deny the accuracy of their navigation.

There were no electronic “fathometers” or radio communications. There was no "Long Range Navigation" (LORAN) system nor "Global Positioning Satellites." Position fixing amounted to their “dead reckoning, a guess, a hunch. If in sight of land they would often rely on a “bearing,” ”Put the stern on the stand-pipe - the bow to the tip of Shot Point and lay the net along the reef that lies there." When they guessed right, they caught fish. If they didn’t - well – they’d better not miss their guess too often.

In 1908, the boys aboard the “Columbia” made a lift of eight tons of herring. Over the season the Andersons had caught and shipped 75 tons of herring they’d caught in the waters near Presque Isle, 10 railroad cars of herring for the markets in the cities.

In 1932 the brothers contracted to have a 56-foot diesel-powered boat built for them by the Koski brothers in Portgage Entry. They named it the "Peter A" after their father who had died in 1921. The “Columbia” was sold to a company that only wanted to salvage its steam engine. The hull of the vessel finally sank somewhere between Gaine's Rock and Ripley Rock in Marquette’s Lower Harbor. Many local folks still remember the "Peter A" and The Anderson’s Fish House (Thill's Fish House is there now).

Jack Anderson, son of John, grandson of Peter and Anna, remembers one fishing trip when he was aboard the "Peter A." It was Easter. They had been fishing out near Stannard Rock, a reef some thirty miles off shore. The shifting fields of ice caught them on their way home, closing in and locking them in place for three days. Nights they could see the Big Bay light over the stern and the light at Granite Rock (another reef off shore) forward. The rest of the world was ice. What did they eat? What do you think? Fish cooked on the cabin stove. They were surrounded by fresh water.

With the passage of time conditions on the lake were changing - and not for the better. The construction of the Welland Ship Canal around Niagara Falls created a passage between Lake Erie and Lake Ontario. In addition to opening the lakes to ocean going ships it had also opened a passage for sea lamprey to migrate into the Great Lakes.

Sea lamprey are an eel-like creature with a disc shaped head and a round "mouth" filled with sharp teeth. Lamprey can attach themselves to the smooth skin of trout and quite literally suck the life out of it. The introduction of this specie would be catastrophic to great lakes fisheries.

In addition the gill nets, nets with multi-looped openings sized to catch the fish behind the gills, were also catching too many under-sized fish. Restrictive rules were enacted to protect the trout population.

With the death of John Anderson in 1953, the Anderson Fish Company closed down. The fish house was sold and the "Peter A" was sold to a party in Grand Marais. The Anderson's record on Lake Superior is an enviable one. Eighty-one years as successful commercial fishermen without the loss of a boat or man. It was the end of an era in Marquette.

Native Americans, Indians with sovereign nation status, are able to continue taking lake trout even though the fish are off-limits to others. It would seem the days of large commercial fishing operations are over.

So take a moment out of your busy day, pause, look out over that Big Water. Watch those steel gray walls of icy water march shoreward flashing their icy grin at you, inviting you to come out and play. Listen to the howl of that cold wind. Think of Peter and Anna, "out there in a rowboat." They were some of the pioneers who made this land what it is.

THE COPPER MINERS

The Survivor

Prologue

This story is based on historic fact! The fundamentals and the hardships endured by the principals are as correct as any historic tale is ever apt to be.

I am not a historian, not a reporter of facts. I'm a teller of stories. Past experience doing research, even among people who had been there and seen it, led to broad variations of the facts. Then, too, it's the winners who write any history - which tends to color the tale somewhat.

In light of these observations I have become a subscriber to this philosophy: Never malign anyone but never let the "facts" get in the way of a good story. I think this is a good story. I hope you agree.

Any reference to any person, living or dead, is purely coincidental.

♎

The Survivor

Isle Royale

Isle Royale: It was called "Minong" by the Indians, a place of evil spirits. The white man saw it as a source of copper. Both were right.

In the Beginning

The year was 1844. The wilderness that was destined to become the Upper Peninsula of Michigan lay green and lush in its natural state. The pristine waters of "*Lac Superiore*," the great inland sea, sparkled and laughed in the summer sunshine. The chortling of the waters on the rocky coastline echoed as it always had, unchanged for thousands of years. Now change had come. A new sound was heard. A surprised exclamation, faint at first, was repeated and soon grew with the passion of its own creation. The cry "Copper!" echoed across the land.

White men were arriving, funneling through the watery pathway at Sault Ste Marie. Word of the mineral deposits, the vast stands of timber, wealth to be torn from this virgin territory, reached the ears of the wealthy and the powerful in the east. Their reaction was swift and predictable: they wanted it.

William Austin Burt was sent across the Straits of Mackinac with instructions to press ever westward. With transit and stakes, measuring chain, solar compass and notebook, Burt set out to walk the length and breadth of this strange land, surveying as he went. The land was being measured, portioned and divided. Lines were being drawn, maps were being created and descriptions to suit the legal nature of the invader were devised. This new country would be evaluated, filed upon, claimed by interests from the financial centers of the east. Lumber barons would stake their claims - or steal them. The remainder would be distributed to the settlers, miners, laborers, and others of the migrant populations. It was the land. There was a promise of wealth. There was opportunity.

The word in the east was, "Go west!"

The native populations had lived in harmony with the land and with nature for hundreds of years. They were looked upon as ignorant and backward savages. The Chiefs of the Ojibwa Nation were overwhelmed by this influx of strangers with their equally strange ways. They spoke an unknown tongue. Their reasoning was not understood. They had a peculiar fetish with owning the land, controlling the water. They brought with them an alcoholic drink, an addictive beverage the Indian did not know and could not control. It degraded them, reduced them to slavish dependence.

The Chiefs tried to adjust to this change, to compromise, to re-stabilize their world. With no understanding of these newcomers, no knowledge of metes and bounds, of legal descriptions, of deeds and money, and even less comprehension of the consequence they unwittingly gave away vast tracts of land. What they were promised was a fraction of its worth, a mere pittance, a nothing. Ironically they wouldn't even receive that. It happened at a grand meeting of all the native peoples with a representative of their "great white father." It was called the Treaty of LaPointe.

In the days that followed the grand meeting life at the small settlement at LaPointe, one island among many islands on the south shore of the Inland Sea, gradually returned to its slow and easy pace. But new developments were afoot. The time of the voyageurs, the explorers, the fur traders, was passing. The newcomers would tear at the earth; chop the forests, build unmoving log huts in clusters, in settlements. Exploitation had begun. Life for the Indians would never be the same.

Charlie Bodine was a French Canadian who had come to LaPointe four years earlier. He and four companions were lured by the promise of wealth and adventure. They trapped, traded, fraternized with the natives, and scrabbled for riches in the fur trade. As time passed it became apparent they were achieving nothing beyond survival. The partnership dissolved in bickering and haggling.

Charlie, as dark haired as the Indians, charismatic, and quick of wit, had established a special relationship with a local Indian family. He had taken a young and attractive Indian maiden, Angelique, to be his wife. The girl had no part in the decision. Her father made the agreement. Charlie paid two iron axes, a fine rifle, four traps, and three blankets. The union was seen as beneficial to the Indian family. It did not occur to the girl to object. Through this union Charlie became the conduit for the furs of many of the Indians.

Each spring fur buyers of John Jacob Astor's American Fur Company came from the east to Mackinac Island. Each spring Charlie and several of the Indians paddled canoes toward the rising sun for twelve days. They paddled beyond the rapids where the whitefish were caught, down the river, and on to Mackinac Island. Charlie joined other traders who congregated there to sell their furs. Charlie usually had three or four canoes loaded with fine pelts, maybe five canoes if it had been a good year.

Angelique had adjusted to her life, learned to keep the white man's house, adjusted to Charlie's ways, submitted to his physical appetites, and stoically endured his occasional frustrations and intoxication. Bodine was not a large or forceful man. With his quick wit, curly black hair, and thin, trim moustache, he made friends quickly. He had an inborn desire for acceptance and a tendency toward compromise. He was not physically abusive although abuse of Indian women was common.

It was the spring that Charlie returned from Mackinac Island with three white men that Angelique went to see the tribal medicine man.

Minong

The white men were searching for the red metal called copper. They needed a guide. They had met Charlie. They were excited, enthusiastic, looking for the big island to the north, called "Minong" by the Indians.

Charlie had invited them to come to LaPointe.

They could start from there. He would be interested in accompanying them. They would discuss it further.

After an evening meal and while seated at the table in the Bodine cabin Charlie and the three men talked of the coming exploration.

"Copper!" Arms extended, hands outstretched, "There are chunks this big! A fella' told me. Pure copper! It's just lying around! It's there for the taking!" They spoke excitedly, describing what they believed they would find.

Angelique cleared the table of the remains of the meal. She gave no indication that she heard or understood their conversation. Behind her impassive dark eyes she knew what was said. She knew of the island of Minong.

Many summers before three young braves, eager for manhood, had set out for that mysterious island. They were anxious to face a mighty enemy, to return victorious. They would have much honor. The medicine man counseled against their venture but the blood of the young braves was hot. They would not be deterred. The night they left the sky had shone blood red. Light had rippled back and forth and leapt and twisted high overhead. The people were afraid.

On the following day a great storm arose in the west and swept across the water. The wind blew savagely tearing foam from the crashing waves. It hurled the flying spray into the thrashing trees along the shore.

It was as the medicine man had warned. The three young braves were never seen again.

Minong was seen as a dark land of evil spirits.

These were the thoughts, the memories behind those dark eyes, as she quietly moved about, listening to the excited conversation.

The Lure of Copper

The men offered Charlie money if he would be their guide.

Charlie waved away the money, bargaining instead for an interest, a share in any minerals that might be found. Angelique would be their cook, would maintain the camp.

After much haggling an agreement was reached. It was sealed with handshakes all around. The men continued talking late into the night. They discussed details of the coming trip, provisions, times, seasons, and the unpredictability of the weather. Angelique quietly slipped out of the cabin and made her way to the Ojibwa encampment.

The medicine man's lodge sat alone, removed a short way from the others. An old man was sitting before a small fire. His face bore the wrinkled countenance of many years exposed to sun and wind. He sat staring into the flames that were reflected in his deep dark eyes.

Angelique quietly sat down opposite. Several minutes passed before he looked at her.

"You will go to Minong, my daughter?"

Angelique said nothing only looked at the fire.

The old man nodded slowly. Three owl feathers hanging in his braided hair shifted slightly across his chest. A small furry black bundle rested on his crossed legs.

"I have been waiting for you." He slowly untied the thong around the bundle. He laid it on the ground and unrolled it. "Here, my daughter is strong medicine. This will help you on your journey." He selected from the objects before him. "This is the paw of the beaver, the creator, to hold you safe from evil. There are three pebbles from the shore of our land to show the spirits that you are only a visitor and that you will return from where you came. These quills from the porcupine will protect you from the wild animals of Minong. This bearskin will give you strength and endurance. And this," he removed one of the feathers from his braided hair and placed it in the bundle, "this feather of the owl will make you wise in times of trial, will help you move swiftly and surely when you cannot clearly see the way."

After a respectful pause Angelique reached into her deerskin pouch and placed a small bag of tobacco on the ground beside the open bundle. Both continued to sit silently watching the fire. Smoke curled upward and disappeared in the darkness. After awhile the old man leaned forward and picked up the bag of tobacco. He removed a pinch and placed the pouch in his lap. Reaching over the fire he gently rubbed his fingers together releasing the tobacco into the flames. Both raised their heads to watch the smoke rise to the Great Manitou. It disappeared into the darkness of a star-filled sky.

The old man resumed his position, staring into the fire. Angelique sat quietly for a time then reached forward, folded, rolled, and tied the bundle. Placing it carefully in her pouch she quietly rose to leave.

"Beware, my daughter, the evil spirits who dwell in that dark land."

Angelique paused, waiting, looking at the old man. He did not speak further nor move nor look up. She bowed her head respectfully, then turned and walked away.

The party departed LaPointe in two large freight canoes. They carried supplies for five people for two months. The three white men were in one canoe. Charlie and Angelique paddled the other. The weather was warm. The great lake was docile. A gentle southwest wind enabled them to set a makeshift sail as they followed the shoreline eastward.

They camped that night on the shore of the Keewenaw Peninsula. The next morning they angled northward across open water with the aid of the same favorable wind. By late afternoon the somber bulk of Minong rose on the horizon. Drawing close to the rocky coast they proceeded east in search of a suitable landing site. The gentle following sea aided their passage. Small waves broke noisily against the rocky shoreline. They came upon a series of small islands as the sun touched the western horizon. With the sky glowing gold, then orange, and changing to red and deeper violet, they approached the rocky shoreline.

With darkness coming on a landing was made on the largest of the islands. A cove among the rocks revealed itself as they drew near. It would provide shelter for the canoes. A campsite was quickly selected in the extended twilight. Charlie and one of the men gathered firewood. The other two set up tents and portaged supplies ashore. Angelique started a fire to prepare something to eat.

By full dark preparations had been completed. The tired men seated themselves around the fire welcoming Angelique's hot beans and flat corn bread washed down with cold water.

A wolf once - twice - a long way off howled, and was silent. An owl hooted nearby. Leaves rustled in the forest. A twig snapped in the darkness outside their circle of firelight. Waves gurgled and chortled against the rocks. They seemed to be chuckling at the growing apprehension of the three white men. They glanced nervously into the darkness and at one another.

Angelique went about quietly and efficiently cleaning up, burning waste, washing implements in the nearby lake. Charlie settled comfortably beside the fire, smoking his pipe, leaning against a stump.

After a brief discussion among themselves the three white men approached Charlie. They insisted that a watch be maintained through the night. The night would be divided into five watches of two hours each. Someone must always be awake, watchful, keeping the fire going. Charlie protested, insisting there was no need. The three would not be pacified. They glanced apprehensively toward the dark forest, listening to the night sounds emanating from the surrounding darkness. They insisted there must be a guard. Angelique would be first, followed by Charlie, then each of them in turn. Feeling that the matter had been settled they went to their tent and tied down the flap.

There was no moon. Stars sparkled like jewels on the black velvet of the heavens. The small cocoon of firelight shown bravely against the encroaching darkness. This strange land, invisible in the night, was a presence to be felt more than seen. It seemed to exude an air of mystery, of foreboding.

Angelique paused, listening. She fingered the pouch containing her medicine bundle before continuing with her work. She stowed and secured all the supplies raising them in a cache safe from any hungry animals of the night.

Charlie, puffing contentedly on his pipe, glanced at Angelique. Their eyes met. Charlie smiled, indicating the men's tent with his pipestem and slowly shook his head.

The only sound emanating from the tent was muffled snoring. The three had been swiftly overcome by the exhaustion of the open-water voyage. Hard paddling for the forty-mile trip had been a constant requirement to supplement the gentle southwest wind. These men from Boston weren't accustomed to that steady muscular strain. In addition the vast reach of the great lake had frightened, intimidated them. The combination of exertion and tension had worn them out. They would sleep the sound sleep of utter exhaustion.

Angelique finished her work and sat quietly across from Charlie. Charlie was nodding, dozing over his pipe. The wolf was silent. The hoot of the owl had faded farther and farther away until it was no more. The fire crackled fitfully. The muffled chatter of the breaking waves broke the stillness. The silence of the stars in the vastness of the dark sky was soothing and restful. Angelique watched the flickering flames, the pulsating glow of the coals. Her fingers gently caressed the bearskin bundle in her pouch.

The crack of a dead branch brought Charlie awake. He yawned, stretched, and casually looked around. Reaching with one arm he picked up a piece of the dry wood and carelessly tossed it on the fire. Sparks swirled upward, disappearing in the darkness.

He saw Angelique watching him. A sudden raising of his head, an inclination toward their tent, and Angelique rose and went to bed. Charlie knocked out his pipe against a rock then leaned back and looked around. The night was beautiful. A thin moon was rising slowly over the eastern horizon. A narrow ribbon of silver danced across the water. Charlie added another stick to the fire, settled back against the stump, and drifted off to sleep.

The morning dawned clear and still. The sliver of moon still hung in the western sky. Charlie awoke with a shiver in the chill morning air. He shrugged and poked up the dying coals. Feeding small, dry twigs followed by heavier wood he soon had the fire blazing. He walked to the water's edge, squatted down and splashed water on his face, shivering slightly at its chill.

Angelique emerged from the tent and lowered the food cache. After removing selected food she raised the bundle and retied the rope. Dipping water from the lake she set some jerky aside to soak. She hung a tin of water over the fire.

Charlie turned over several rocks lying on the moist earth. Picking up a few worms and grubs he threaded one onto a stiff hooked wire he had tied to a thin line. He tossed the offering into the water. Squatting comfortably on the bank he waited.

Angelique added coffee to the boiling water. She had slid an iron frying pan across the hot rocks of the fire and added a small piece of salted suet.

The sun cleared the horizon chasing the last wisps of mist from the sheltered waters. Angelique squatted beside the fire mixing flour, salt, and water into a dough for biscuits. The growing warmth of the sun on her back felt good.

A tent flap was thrown back suddenly and one of the white men emerged in his underwear. Blinking owl-eyed in the sunshine he yawned, stretched, and scratched himself.

Charlie walked back to the fire and tossed several nice trout on the ground beside Angelique. Wordlessly she picked up a knife and began cleaning them.

The man in the underwear stared, shivered suddenly, and ducked back into the tent.

"Brian! Don! Roll out! Trout for breakfast."

The muffled sounds of men stirring, cursing in the morning chill, came from the closed tent. One by one they emerged.

The first one out, Donald Engstrom, was a well built man about 30 with the blonde hair and blue eyes of his Scandinavian ancestry. His companion, Reginald Smith, was about the same age, an inch or so shorter, and 30 pounds lighter with brown hair and hazel eyes. The two had been working together for several years. Their backgrounds in minerals and metallurgy dated back to their years in school together. Word of copper finds in the Northwest

Territory had attracted them. They investigated, convinced a group of investors in Boston to finance their expedition, and came to the great lakes region.

A condition of their financial support was the third member of the group, Brian Hogue. He was an intense little man, an accountant by profession, and an employee of one of the investors. Hogue was to monitor expenses, make periodic reports, and assist in whatever way Don Engstrom, the team leader, requested. Hogue's report making was frustrated by the lack of any form of message delivery since they had left Sault Ste. Marie - "the Soo."

"Charlie! Dammit, why didn't you wake us last night?"

Charlie looked over, grinned, and shrugged his shoulders. "I sit by the fire." Charlie pointed. "Nothing she was there. Sleep, my fran,' sleep."

Hogue, the last one out, fumbled with a pair of iron-rimmed eyeglasses then peered about with the suspicious squint that seems common to members of his profession.

Charlie's answer was accepted with a degree of uncertainty. The three turned abruptly and walked to the waters edge to wash up. The sun's rays grew stronger, warmer. The last wisps of mist vanished. The warmth drove the chill away. The waters of the lake sparkled like a myriad of diamonds while the crackle of frying fish attracted the hungry men. All indications promised a beautiful day.

Returning to the fire the three huddled around the warmth. They poured themselves coffee from the tin pail. Angelique deftly turned the fish while biscuits baked under a bark reflector on a rock. After Don and Redge and Brian had been served, Charlie filled his plate and joined them. Angelique cooked the remainder of the dough and fried the remaining fish before she, too, sat down by herself and ate.

Over a second cup of coffee the men gathered around a roughly sketched map of the island. Don and Redge discussed rock structure and the promise of one site over another based on the crude drawing. Charlie scrutinized the chart then the island rising beyond attempting to match the two. Brian just watched and listened.

It was decided that Don and Charlie would take one canoe and explore to the east. Redge and Brian would take the other and go west. Refinements in details would be noted for future addition to their crude chart. Any area that showed promise of copper would be noted for further discussion that evening.

Angelique would remain at the campsite preparing it as a base of operations. The canoes were hastily unloaded, leaving the sorting and storage for Angelique. The men stuffed several strips of jerky in their pockets and were away.

The Exploration

Angelique picked up, washed up, and then busied herself arranging the supplies. She sorted foodstuff from clothing. The food was placed in individual sacks, tied shut, and hung from branches 20 or 30 feet in the air. Suspended midway the food would be safe from predators.

The sun was directly overhead when she finished. Walking down the rocky shoreline she discovered a pool of trapped water that had been warmed by the sun. Removing her clothing she bathed and rinsed her clothing. She spread her clothing over nearby bushes and stretched out on a warm rock in the sun. As she dozed in the warm sunshine the light breeze gently dried her clothing. Later she gathered firewood that she stacked near the campfire pit. With that done she spent the afternoon exploring parts of the island.

The sun was low in the west and the air was cooling when the first of the canoes returned. Redge and Brian dragged ashore tired and hungry. The two immediately headed for the tent but found it uncomfortably warm inside. The two lay down on the soft needles under a nearby pine tree. They quickly fell asleep. A short time later Don and Charlie returned. They too were tired and hungry. No one had found any sign of copper. Discouragement hung heavy in the air.

Angelique broke up the pre-soaked jerky. She added some cattail root she had dug in a nearby marsh that afternoon. Adding a few chopped wild leeks, and a little salt, some flour to thicken the mix and allowed it to simmer. Biscuits were rising on a hot rock beside the fire.

Don and Redge pored over the island chart comparing notes and noting refinements. Charlie and Brian silently looked on.

"That east end is pretty rugged. Points and inlets everywhere."

Redge nodded understanding. "The coastline is rocky to the west too. There's an inlet down there a mile or so. It's not apparent until you're up close. It opens up to a nice bay - a small lake actually.

"Did you get to look around?"

"No! We checked from the mouth but didn't have time to look further. I think we should both go down there tomorrow."

"Why not move the campsite down there?"

Charlie took the pipe from his mouth. "Le's doan be so quick for move de camp." He casually waved the pipe stem, "This, she be pretty good place. The breeze drive away zee bugs," he smiled. "Wan mile, she not be so far in canoe."

Don and Redge looked at one another, shrugged. "OK," Don responded. "We'll camp here and paddle down to your bay, Redge."

"That sounds like a good plan. And, say,

something smells awfully good."

Charlie turned toward Angelique who nodded her head. "My franz," said Charlie, "iz ready to eat!"

The four men struggled to their feet and shuffled to the fire. Angelique filled their bowls in turn. Each found a comfortable spot and sat down heavily. Darkness thickened as they ate. The men went to bed immediately upon finishing their meal. Charlie was fast asleep where he sat. Angelique cleaned up around the fire and went to bed.

When the rising sliver of moon looked down on the scene the throbbing coals of the dying fire were all that remained. Charlie woke with a shiver, retired to the tent, and all was quiet.

A skunk wandered aimlessly into the campsite. It sniffed inquisitively around the cooking area. Finding that Angelique had left nothing for him the skunk wandered off into the darkness.

Days followed one on another with the men going off to search each day. Angelique had the campsite so organized that she had free time to explore the island herself. There were several days when all four men went in one canoe. Angelique was then able to explore the coastline and neighboring islands. She became familiar with the location of marshes, roots, berries and animal sign. It was the way she had been raised; it was her way of life.

The men returned each night tired and discouraged. They ate mechanically and silently. The moon grew to full and waned and disappeared. No one noticed.

After five weeks of exploration ranging along the coastline and inland all they had to show for it were several small samples of native copper. As they discussed these finds over supper, examined their samples, Angelique watched and listened. Later that night she told Charlie what she had seen on an adjacent island; a large rock of that same copper material the men had been examining.

The next morning Charlie told Don and Redge what Angelique had said.

"What? Where? Geeezus, Charlie, that's what we're lookin' for. Where is it?"

Charlie turned to Angelique. "Where she is, mon cher?"

Angelique rose and started walking west along the shore. The four men quickly gathered a few things and followed. It took just over an hour until they arrived at a large powder-green boulder under the trees near the rocky beach. The boulder was pure copper.

After a brief examination Don and Redge looked at one another in amazement.

"This is it!" Don threw the chart into the air.

"Hoorah!" shouted Redge

Brian looked on noncommittally. Charlie sat down and began to fill his pipe.

Don and Redge were inspired with a new vigor.

Everything seemed to have urgency. The crude map was marked with the approximate location of the claim. A stone cairn was erected. Time became important. They had been on the island almost six weeks. They must get supplies. They had to record their claim in Detroit. They would need men and tools and equipment. They could send a message to their backers to tell them the good news. They would need a fresh injection of capital, cash. They could get supplies at the Soo. Someone must stay to guard the claim 'til spring, 'til the others could return. Whoever remained would need supplies immediately. It was nearly September.

It was decided. Charlie and Angelique would return, remain through the winter. They could build a semi-permanent camp at their present site and spend the winter on the island.

First everyone would go to the Soo. Don and Redge would continue to Detroit to register the claim and arrange for men and equipment to return in the spring. Brian would remain at the Soo, purchase supplies for Charlie and Angelique, and await the equipment sent north by Don and Redge. Charlie and Angelique would return immediately with supplies to Minong.

Two days after discovering Angelique's copper rock the party cached their remaining supplies and all departed for the Soo.

Regroup

They were eight days enroute to the Soo. The evening of the seventh day, gathered around their campfire on the tip of Whitefish point, they once more reviewed their plans. Don Engstrom began.

"Gentlemen, we should arrive in the Soo tomorrow afternoon. Our priorities, as I see them, are," he ticked them off on his fingers, "Redge, you and I must record the claim without delay. We must get money for development in the spring. We have to purchase equipment, tools, and supplies. We'll assemble it all at the Soo. Brian, you'll stay at the Soo and collect our gear as it arrives. We'll hire men in the spring and bring them with us. Brian, you'll be ready with transportation to go to Isle Royale as early as possible in the spring."

Redge nodded in agreement. "We have the claim located sufficiently to be recorded. Austin Burt is still far from the mine with his pin setting. Unless their attitude in Detroit has changed we should be able to secure ownership without any problem."

Brian Hogue was shaking his head. Both looked askance at him.

"You have yet to ascertain the value of the find."

Don Engstrom sat bolt upright. "We have the samples! Pure Copper! What do you mean 'ascertain the value?' Hell, man, there it is!"

Hogue nodded, "Yes, you have a few pieces broken from the one boulder. What if that's the only copper there?"

Redge raised his hands in frustrated supplication.

Don was beside himself. "Brian, your part in this is as an accountant. We, Redge and I, are the prospectors, the mineralogists. It is we, Redge and I, who decide whether or not we've found copper."

Brian stubbornly shook his head. "I am to send reports!"

"Yes, yes, reports on the handling and balance of our funds. By the way . . ."

"Yes!" Hogue interrupted, "But I am to give my opinion also. I was specifically charged to . . ."

"Okay! Okay!" Redge broke in. "Don, I see no reason Brian can't send a separate message expressing his views. If he feels that is his responsibility to his employer, so be it."

Don turned to Hogue. "Is that satisfactory?"

"If I send it by separate post."

This announcement was greeted with silence.

"All right," Don nodded wearily. "How are our funds? Do we have approval to purchase winter supplies for Charlie and his wife? "

Hogue, still defiant, snapped back, "I think I

can handle that."

"Then it's agreed. Redge and I will arrange passage to Detroit as quickly as possible. After recording the claim we'll contact Boston," turning to nod to Hogue, "advising them of your dissenting opinion . . ."

Hogue raised a hand, "Inform them of my report being forwarded by mail."

Don nodded, "And that your written report has been posted. May I add that our expenses to date have been far below our estimates?"

Hogue, listening intently, nodded agreement. "Yes! We've done very nicely."

"Yes, well, thank you. I'm sure we will be able to sell our find to Boston. Now! Can we agree that none of this," he looked sharply at both companions, motioned to include Charlie and Angelique, "is to be discussed with anyone else! No one! Not in the Soo, not in Detroit - other than the recorder. No one other than our backers in Boston!"

Both companions nodded.

"I want to hear you say it."

Redge looked up sharply to receive a slight inclination of the head toward Hogue.

Redge spread his hands. "I won't talk to anyone."

Brian added, "And I won't either." Looking up he saw his companions waiting. "I won't talk to anyone about this either. There! Will that do it?"

All turned toward Charlie and Angelique.

Charlie shrugged, "But of course not."

The three looked toward Angelique. Charlie noticed in surprise. "Ha, my franz, she will not speak of it, even with me," he chuckled.

Don looked wearily from Redge to Brian. "Look, we've been pushing pretty hard. We're all tired. Fuses are getting a little short." He waved a hand in the air in resignation, "Let's put this flare up behind us. Tomorrow we'll be in the Soo. Let's take an evening for a hot bath, a good meal, and a night's sleep. We'll all feel better for it. Agreed?"

His two companions sat silently for a moment or two.

"Yes," Hogue nodded, "I agree. I could use a bath."

"Count me in," answered Redge, "and I agree, too. Brian could use a bath.

Brian's head jerked around to look at Redge who was grinning at him. All three broke into laughter.

Don stretched, yawned, and turned to his blankets. "A hot bath!" he murmured dreamily, "I could sure use one of those."

Supplies

The arrival of two more canoes at the Soo was

not a major event. It was September and leaves were beginning to change color. Thoughts of the approaching winter were on everyone's mind. There was a sense of urgency everywhere. Boats of all sizes were arriving and departing daily.

The Soo, with its location at the head of Lake Superior, was the focal point for all traffic, coming and going. The intensity of the trade would steadily increase until the cold, the storms, and the ice drove everyone to shelter. It would hold them with a frigid grip. Only the return of the sun, the warm breezes of spring could break the stillness of a northern winter.

Some would be caught out in the freeze up. Some few always were. They would stretch their luck against the weather. Sailors in a wooden scow - or voyageurs in canoes - would pay a severe price for that lost gamble. The supplies they carried meant the difference between life and death to those further up the lake. If they lost, so did others. It was the way of this Northwest Territory.

The following morning three men made their way to the docks east of town. That was where the boats from Detroit and the east were moored. A lively trade was under way between boat captains and crowds of people clamoring for anything and everything available. Barter was booming with furs comprising a large portion of the return cargoes. Disappointed frontiersmen often were forced to sell their furs, pocket the cash, and look elsewhere - or wait for the next ship.

Passage south was easily arranged for Mr. Donald Engstrom and Mr. Reginald Smith, land speculators, aboard a vessel that would clear the harbor within the hour. The third member of their party remained in the dock area, unobtrusively observing the hustle and bustle of commerce. He was appalled at the apparent lack of order, at the prices that were offered for goods. The strong demand for supplies, especially foodstuffs, interested him.

Captain Jesse Strong wearily concluded the transactions that disposed of his remaining cargo. His crewmen were stowing baled furs below decks in preparation for the return trip. Captain Strong was walking toward the gangway on his way to his cabin when a short intense man wearing iron-rimmed glasses approached him.

"Excuse me, Captain?"

Strong turned, looking down at the man questioningly. "Yes?"

"I see that you have unloaded your ship, sold your goods."

Squinting at the sky, attempting to divine the weather and impatient with this statement of the obvious, he nodded and answered curtly, "Yes, I have."

"Will you be making another trip? That is, will you be returning with more supplies?"

Tiring of this frequently asked question and

anxious to gather his personal effects for a night ashore he responded rather abruptly, "Yes, God permitting."

Sensing impatience Hogue inquired, "Will you be spending the night? Perhaps we could meet later to our mutual advantage?"

This suggestion of advantage caused the Captain to look more keenly at this frontier clad individual with the educated city vocabulary. "Maybe we could. Where are you staying?"

"I have a room at the Chippewa Hotel."

"Well! I've got a room there too."

"That's most fortunate. Would it be convenient to meet," he snapped open a watch, glanced at it, and added, "in, say, three hours? At six o'clock at the hotel bar?"

The captain appraised this short, stout man who spoke with such assurance. "Yes - yes, that'd be fine."

Hogue smiled broadly. "Thank you, Captain." He extended his hand that the Captain automatically grasped, "'til six o'clock then."

Brian Hogue walked briskly away from a very puzzled ship captain.

By the time accountant Brian Hogue met Captain Jesse Strong that evening in the crude barroom of the Chippewa Hotel he had spoken to two other ship Captains and had a 7:30 appointment with a fourth.

The discussion with Captain Strong was going

well after his experience with two prior negotiations.

"So, you see, Captain, you bring the supplies from Detroit. I will buy them from you at the price we agree upon here," indicating the figures on the document before them. "If possible I will pay you in furs. You can re-sell the fur later at whatever price you choose. You will turn a profit at both ends of your trip without the trouble and delay of disposing of your cargo. My interest is in the food and clothing that will be sent up the lake."

Examining the contract Captain Strong could see that the price was generous. "And what will bind this contract?"

"An agreed upon amount - ten percent of the contract - to be held by a third party, paid to you if you deliver by the date you have stated. That amount is yours contingent upon your return with the goods. But it will be applied to the agreed purchase price if I am here to receive the shipment. If you fail to return by the stated time, the deposit reverts to me."

"Who is this third party?"

"The president of the Superior Bank branch here in the Soo. That's his signature confirming that the money will be on deposit under the conditions stated."

Strong squinted as he held the paper near the lamplight. "That appears to be Surridge's signature," he pointed. "See that flourish?" he glanced over at Hogue. "I brought John Surridge out here, you see. I know the man." He bent over the document and scrawled his name.

Hogue folded the paper, slid it into the inner pocket of his coat, and shook hands. "Thank you, Captain. I believe we have entered a mutually profitable agreement. When you arrive on or before October fifth you can expect to have a return cargo waiting on the dock."

"Mr. Hogue, I'll be there!"

By nine o'clock that evening Brian Hogue had purchased $16,780.00 worth of food, clothing, and equipment. This purchase would represent approximately three quarters of the total supplies that would pass through Sault Ste Marie that season. The purchase was secured by the deposit of 10% of the pledged amount, approximately $1,700.00, taken from the balance of $2,162.43 in the mining venture account. When Lake Superior froze shut for the season, Brian Hogue hoped to have sufficient money to return to Boston and open his own offices. These transactions, plus what he would require for his own living expenses, did not allow much for supplying Charlie and Angelique. He could manage to get them some basic requirements now. What the hell, they lived like Indians. The woman was an Indian. Maybe more could be sent later - depending on the market.

Hogue strode down to the shore where Charlie and Angelique were camping. He found them sitting beside a small campfire. Charlie looked up silently as he approached. Angelique remained impassive.

"Charlie, in the morning you come by the hotel. These are the supplies I was able to get." He went through the list of goods he had purchased.

Charlie drew back in surprise. "Mon dieu! This is not enough for zhe wintair. We mus' have, I say, at least two times as much, especially zhe meat and zhe beans."

"Yes, yes, I realize that. This is all that was available. There is no more."

"Well," Charlie sat back, "we will wait."

"There are too many going up the lake. Someone might stumble on our copper. You must go back immediately."

"Without zhe food to eat, zhey will be stumble on our bones before zhe spring she comes. We will wait."

"Charlie, you must go in the morning with what we have. I'll arrange to send more to you as soon as another supply ship arrives from down below."

Charlie removed the pipe from his mouth and stared hard at the other man. "The time, she grow short. Soon come zhe storm, zhe ice."

"You'll get the supplies. I've got the list."

He stared into the bowl of his pipe and then looked up. "You will send supplies?"

"Yes!"

"The storm," he waved the pipe stem toward the western sky, "she come damn quick."

"Charlie, you'll get the supplies you need. I swear it!"

Charlie looked at him, then, grudgingly, nodded. He watched Brian's back through narrowed eyes as the man disappeared toward the settlement. They would need those additional supplies - badly.

Hogue thought briefly about the Bodines as he hurried to his hotel room. He'd send them supplies. Later. After he had completed his transactions. After all the man's wife was an Indian. She would know how to live off the land. With a little luck it would all work out. If it didn't, well, he was a French-Canadian Squaw-man and she was just an Indian.

The Plan

Don Engstrom and Redge Smith left the boat in Detroit with the immediate aim of registering the claim. The legal description presented a problem. They knew where the mine would be. They even had a rough description of where on the island of Minong it was located. Austin Burt and his surveying party were still far to the east aligning and measuring and marching through the wilderness. They fabricated a metes and bounds measurement working a narrative description in between the imaginary figures. No one would be able to prove or disprove the location of the claim by this description but it would satisfy the filing requirements. They could return to re-file when the legal description had been established.

They presented their filing to the clerk with all the confidence and assurance they could muster. It worked. The recorder accepted their filing. It was done!

They next searched for materials for the proposed spring mining. Much of what they would need was not readily available at this outpost of civilization. They arranged orders for spring delivery of explosives, stone drills, hammers, shovels, picks, wheelbarrows, tents, cots, blankets and the myriad of incidentals related to mines and mining.

Discovering a ship sailing eastbound the pair decided to once more divide their group. Don Engstrom hurried to get aboard. He would go east, to Boston, to sell their mining project in person. Redge Smith would stay in Detroit to wait out the spring. He would continue to gather supplies to be sent to the Soo.

In eight years of prospecting and promoting Don and Redge had learned the necessity of "stroking" the investors.

The Investment

Captain Strong returned to Sault Ste. Marie to find that his partner, Brian Hogue, had the markets firmly in his grip. He had contracted with the trappers securing their furs at a set price. His agreement with the shipping Captains established the value of their cargos. With control of nearly all supplies up-bound and setting the fur prices to pay for them he controlled the market.

There was no delay in transferring the ship's cargo. Wagons were lined up at the dock eager to load and move away. Packets of furs were stacked and ready to load. At the west end of town, along the shore of Lake Superior, sailing ships and freight canoes awaited the wagons. Brian Hogue had hired three local bookkeepers to record supplies off loaded, furs on loaded, wagon assignments, and supply recipients. Guards accompanied each wagon to insure security.

Hogue hade found it necessary to acquire the services of a personal bodyguard, a hulking French-Canadian woodcutter, not too smart but notorious among the bars as a brawler. Hogue frequently carried large sums of money. He had also angered much of the local population with low prices for furs and high prices for supplies. Many who needed the supplies badly were unable to pay. They offered to pledge next year's furs as security. These offers were universally rejected. The demands of those with cash in hand showed no sign of diminishing.

Many of the buyers were themselves operators of trading establishments. They would pass the increased costs on to their buyers. They would offer credit against next fall's furs. One man who controlled the market had disrupted the balance of trade.

The monopoly created by Brian Hogue would spread hardship to every settler and trading post on Lake Superior.

Charlie and Angelique leisurely paddled west along the shoreline. They stopped for a day at a trading post on Grand Island. An Englishman named Abraham Williams ran it. Unexpectedly there were friends there who were from LaPointe. They, too, were expecting supplies that had not arrived.

Charlie noted the empty shelves at the Grand Island post. His eyes narrowed again as he thought of Brian Hogue, their half empty canoe and the man's promise to send supplies "as soon as a ship arrives." He turned and saw Angelique watching him. He knew Hogue would probably not send the supplies. And he knew she knew.

His hand moved to his belt. He felt the sheath knife. If the supplies did not come, he, Charlie Bodine, would kill him. In his heart Charlie knew he would be called upon to carry out that promise.

The Dream

The morning of October 29 saw ice pellets

blowing horizontally down the streets. Buyers were still bidding for the few remaining sacks of flour, bags of beans, sides of salt pork. Prices rose even higher. Coffee was nonexistent and had been for weeks. The account of one Brian Hogue at the Superior Bank, Northwest Branch, in Sault Ste. Marie indicated a balance of $59,847.68. Deducting the original $1,700.00 this represented a profit of approximately $58,000.00.

He was already visualizing his Boston Office. "Hogue" in large gilt lettering on the door, "accountants" in much smaller letters underneath.

All thought of copper mining, of Charlie and Angelique Bodine, of an icy island in the vast expanse of Lake Superior, had long since vanished. Here was the money he needed to establish his ambition, to set him up in a lucrative profession far from the hardships of a rustic frontier. Thoughts of a house - on the hill, of course - of magnificent proportion came to his mind. The financial establishments of Boston would compete with each other to lend money to the proprietor of a prominent accounting firm - especially with cash reserves in the amount now in his hands.

Living expenses in the Soo, 'til he could depart aboard one of the early vessels in the spring, would, of course, be paid from the mining venture capital account.

Preparation

The log walls were partially raised. Charlie and Angelique had worked long hours cutting, skidding, and peeling logs. It took both of them to roll the logs up an incline to raise the wall. While Charlie notched them to fit Angelique gathered and stored firewood.

Mornings were chill, frosty. Leaves took on glorious colors. Large V's of migrating geese passed overhead, murmuring and cackling as they flew south. Ducks, too, were passing on their trip south. Twisting and turning as they landed in the coves and inlets, quacking to one another as they fed.

Charlie paused, wiping his sweating brow as he looked up at the majestic geese. He glanced toward Angelique waiting patiently at the end of the log.

"Ah, mon cher, I would like to follow them," raising his hand skyward. "At least so far as La Pointe, eh?"

Angelique did not reply.

Charlie shook his head as he leaned on the pry-pole. The log began to move. Angelique strained, keeping pace.

Angelique was worried. She wanted Charlie to hunt, to gather food for the coming winter. He was intent on finishing the cabin, assuring her that the coming supplies would be more than enough to see them through the winter. He insisted she gather firewood when she wasn't helping move logs.

Evenings beside the fire, while Charlie fell into an exhausted sleep, Angelique sat quietly holding her medicine bundle staring at the fire. She did not trust the white man. She had seen and her father had said, "The white man's promise is like the fluff on the thistle. A puff of air and it is gone. He speaks with the forked tongue." Angelique was afraid.

It was October before the cabin walls were complete. The roof was framed and braced. Charlie was shingling the roof with pieces of bark, tying each one in place. Frost was thick on the ground each morning. Charlie now felt a sense of urgency. He hurried with his work. He frequently paused, looking across the water, hoping to see an approaching canoe, their much-needed supplies. The horizon remained unbroken.

Angelique, too, felt an urgency - to gather food. She was almost frantic digging roots in the cold marsh waters. A few hazelnuts and acorns had escaped the notice of foraging animals. All these things she eagerly gathered. She set out several fishing lines, checking them periodically. Fish were immediately cleaned and set out on racks to dry. Early one morning a young doe was standing at the waters edge. Charlie was able to bring it down with one shot. Angelique dressed and skinned the carcass. She cut the meat into thin strips, salted and hung them inside a low enclosure built over a small fire. The trapped smoke and heat from the fire dried and seasoned the meat.

Charlie no longer insisted that Angelique work on the cabin. If they were going to leave, go to LaPointe, they would have to leave quickly. Winter storms would soon lash out piling ice along the shore. Waves of 20 and 30 feet would destroy anything not safely ashore. No one could then venture onto the lake.

On October 28 the decision was taken out of Charlie's hands. The temperature dropped as a cold front from the far reaches of the Arctic Ocean rolled across the lake. All but the most hardy stored their canoes and ships securely to the shore. Those few who ventured even short distances along the shoreline did so in peril of their lives - and some would pay that price.

The Investors

Arriving in Boston Don arranged lodging. He then contacted Harold McNeil at the offices of Boston Bank and Trust. He was requested to come by immediately.

During the voyage and the overland trip Don had reviewed, examined, projected, reviewed his figures, and examined again. He knew his presentation inside and out. The only variable in the plan was the spring break up - the time they could return to the mine.

McNeil was a heavyset middle-age man, balding, and with penetrating blue eyes. Upon meeting with him Don discovered that Hogue's report had preceded him. His posture and attitude, seated behind his large banker's desk, seemed designed to intimidate, to put visitors on the defensive. Don's no-nonsense presentation, including the rich assay report and the samples of pure copper, invoked an enthusiasm difficult to conceal. McNeil couldn't resist holding the copper in his hand, rubbing the polished metal with his thumb.

In addition to describing remote and dismal mining prospects Hogue's letter had strongly criticized the financial arrangements made with Charlie Bodine. In conceding a share of the discovery, especially now in light of the promising assay report, the amount seemed exorbitant. McNeil asked how he could justify his action.

"We needed a reliable and knowledgeable guide. He was the only one available. There were others who would have taken the job but none who were sufficiently familiar with the lake and the island."

"Hogue says he wasn't familiar with the island? That no one was?"

Don began to experience some irritation at this quibbling over arrangements. This find promised to make rich men of these investors and this man was quarreling with him over pennies.

"Sir, you sent me there to find copper. I did. Now you're criticizing how I did it?"

"But a share . . ."

"Shares, five shares."

"All right! Shares! Five shares in the operation. This is turning out to be one expensive guide. After all, he's just a Frenchman from up north - married to an Indian."

"Well, he's our Frenchman and our Indian. It was his wife, after all - this Indian - who located the vein, the primary outcropping. If not for her we may not have found it 'til next spring. Maybe not then. Thanks to her we'll be shipping copper in the spring."

"When? When do you project your first shipments?"

"It's all right there, in the report. As soon as the weather allows we will return. We'll be shipping copper within that month. Hopefully in April."

The two men looked at each other, searching the other's attitude, looking for any sign of weakness in the other's resolve.

"I'll call a meeting of the group. You present this report to them along with your projections. We'll discuss the guide arrangement again at that time."

"I'm not sure I understand what there is to discuss. The deal has been made."

McNeil rose from his padded chair, gathered the report and handed it across the desk. Walking around he patted the younger man on the shoulder as he led him to the door. "We'll see what happens at the meeting tomorrow. I'll let you know the time."

Dig In

The first storm of the season came from the northwest. The cabin was up and roofed and its shelter was welcome. The hastily constructed fire pit provided heat and the only light inside. The bulk of the big island offered protection to the little cabin huddled on the south side of its east end. The winds and waves hammered the north shore but bypassed their small island.

It blew for three days before Charlie and Angelique dared venture out for anything more than firewood. They learned to keep ahead with the firewood, as it was necessary for the rain-wet wood to dry for several hours before it could be burned. During these days in the dark interior of the windowless cabin they had occasion to catalogue their meager supplies. They considered the coming winter isolation and examined their future. There was not enough food. Hunting and foraging became an immediate priority - if the weather would permit. The probability of receiving supplies was no more. It would take an unseasonable turn of weather and a complete fool to try to cross the lake at this time of year.

Charlie stared into the fire, shivering as the grisly truth bored home. Damn that white man to hell! The Indians were right! Never trust the white man. His hand strayed, almost unconsciously, to the handle of his knife. That time would come. For now, they had to survive. In spite of his continuing resolve to concentrate on the conditions at hand, his mind continued to stray to his hatred of Brian Hogue and his resolve to kill him.

Angelique watched and understood. She gently stroked her medicine bundle as she waited for his reaction. What would they do?

Mission Accomplished

The winds howled down the main street of the little village of Sault Ste Marie. The rapids of the Saint Mary river leaped and steamed in the subzero air. Snow streamed down the road like a moving river, twisting around abandoned barrels and curling up alleyways between buildings. The sign on the Chippewa Hotel clattered against the false building front.

Inside the hotel, beside a roaring fire sat Brian Hogue, drink in hand. His newly acquired wealth had brought him attention. He received prompt service. The respect he received was for the perceived wealth he controlled.

All that remained was to receipt the supplies and materials that would arrive in the spring. When those two mining engineers, those prospectors, arrived he intended to turn the supplies over to them and wash his hands of this whole operation. His final report would give no indication of his temporary use of funds but would indicate the disposition of funds dispersed in regard to the mining venture. It would reflect a comfortable balance remaining in the account. This should assure him of the continued handling of the Boston accounting service after he had established his own offices.

There had been vociferous objections, indeed, several threats over his having cornered the market on winter supplies In the end they had paid his price. It was that or starve. Brian retained his bodyguard whenever he ventured outside the hotel. He took the precaution of avoiding dark alleys and lonely environments where he might be vulnerable. Once back in Boston these ignorant frontier people would be nothing but a memory.

Shelter

The afternoon and evening of November fifth saw an end of the rain and sleet and a gradual reduction in the force of the wind. Cloud cover moved off to the east. With darkness came glittering stars and a bitter cold. Charlie and Angelique held each other close under their bearskin robe. Several times during the night the chill drove Charlie out from under the robe to add wood to the fire.

With the dawn a weak sun shown on glittering ice crystals, ice crystals that covered everything in sight. Ice sheathed much of the rock along the shoreline. The wind had subsided. The waves had moderated but sullenly reflected the cold steel blue of the sky. Charlie took the rifle, paddled to the main island, and went in search of game. Angelique took a birch bark basket and went into the woods searching for moss and lichen with which to chink cracks in the cabin walls. She also dug up some cattail roots she came upon and gathered acorns in a protected grove of oak trees.

The sun was low in the west when Charlie returned. The temperature was again below freezing and dropping. He had seen no game, hadn't eaten since breakfast, and was bone tired. Angelique made a hot soup of salt, suet and cattail root thickened slightly with flour. Charlie ate wearily, crawled under the bearskin robe, and was quickly asleep.

Angelique returned to searching out and filling cracks in the walls. She would feel for the cold drafts and fill the openings with moss. Firelight flickered across the cabin walls. When the supply of moss was exhausted she wearily sat down beside the fire.

Staring into the flickering flames she watched the throbbing coals. They were almost like a heartbeat. Gently, unconsciously, she fingered her medicine bundle. Finally, with a sigh of frustration, she added wood to the fire and crawled under the robe with Charlie. Outside the night was still and clear. An owl hooted forlornly - once - and was silent.

The Shares

At the meeting of the investment group Don Engstrom once again presented the figures and his projections for shipping copper.

The group heartily approved of his report and projections. They passed the copper samples around among themselves, admiring them. They too were critical of the arrangement made with Charlie Bodine. Hogue's report seemed to indicate that his interest was a concession needlessly made. They discussed the point with particular attention directed to the dollar difference between the estimated wages and the return accruing to the five shares. They turned to their lawyer, a Mr. Ashbrook Smithers who was the senior partner of Smithers and Smithers, for advice.

The lawyer, a tall slender man with delicate features, very properly groomed and well dressed, questioned Don concerning documentation.

"Documentation?"

"Ah, yes. Was there a written document? A binding contract?"

Don held out his right hand so all could see. "Right there! There was the contract! We discussed, we argued, Redge and I offered, Charlie agreed, and we shook hands."

The counsel looked down, examining his cuticles. "Sir, you have no contract. Since there is no documentation," he shrugged, "there is no contract. You must have a signed, witnessed agreement."

Don looked around the table in frustration. Board member's expressions were impassive. He leaned forward, hands on the table, looking down at the floor.

"Sir!" Turning once more toward the attorney, "Redge and I both agreed to this arrangement. Doesn't that constitute a witnessed agreement? Take your pick. Either Redge or I could be the witness."

"Mr. Engstrom, It would appear that your sympathy in this matter lies with the Bodines. This would make you, in so far as this matter is concerned, what could be referred to - please don't take offense - referred to as hostile. It was, after all, your arrangement. In this matter, you and Mr. Smith were acting jointly - together. There was, legally, one entity. There was no witness."

Don stared in amazement at the attorney. There was no passion in his expression, no malice. He was simply stating, creating a legal position. Justice, ethics and morality were not a part of this man's thinking. Like a prostitute he had consciously forsworn any consideration of right or wrong to satisfy the desires of his client, this copper consortium. And he did it for money.

"Gentlemen," Don addressed the group. "I need to assemble additional information. Could we postpone a decision on this matter?"

McNeil looked up in surprise, glanced around the table, lingering momentarily on the lawyer who shrugged imperceptibly. "I - ah - don't understand but, if you feel it is necessary, we can allow it. Gentlemen," he gaveled the table one time, "we are adjourned."

Don nodded, "Thank you."

As the group gathered their notes, passed a few comments among themselves, and left the room Don remained standing at the table - staring down at his notes - with no idea what he was going to do.

Food

The day dawned clear. The sun seemed stronger with a promise of some slight warming trend. Charlie again took the rifle and the canoe and headed for the main island. Angelique ground and began leaching the acorns. Leaving them to soak in the water she returned to the woods to gather moss to complete the chinking of the cabin. About mid morning a shot rang out. She paused to look in the direction of the sound. She waited, listening hard. Nothing! Maybe Charlie had been lucky. Maybe they would eat meat tonight. Unconsciously her mittened hand sought out her medicine bundle.

By mid-afternoon Charlie returned with the hide and a quarter of a moose he had shot. He had cleaned the animal, saving the heart and liver. He would leave what he had in the canoe and go back to get the rest of the carcass. There would be meat to eat tonight.

The cabin was now as complete as was practicable. The entrance was low and covered with a tightly woven mat of reeds. The smoke hole in the roof was constructed with an external cover to keep out rain and an adjustable flap. The openings between the logs were tightly chinked with moss and lichen.

There had been much wood easily available, fallen trees in the forest and driftwood along the shore. Charlie had helped but Angelique had gathered and stacked most of it while Charlie had built the cabin. In examining their situation, supplies, and equipment their most critical need was food. If they were to survive they would have to provide for themselves. Charlie would concentrate on game. He had set several deadfall traps. Half a dozen snares were set in likely places along small game trails. Angelique would collect what nuts and roots she could find. The meat would have to be smoked, preserved for the months ahead.

In the days that followed Charlie killed a wolf with the rifle, trapped four partridge, and caught an even dozen rabbits. Angelique had constructed a hood over the fire and a wooden rack on which to hang and smoke the meat. They had caught eighteen trout that they filleted and smoked.

Snow now covered the land. Ice was beginning to close in the waters of the lake. Some of their meat had frozen. This she wrapped in leaves, and buried under snow in a rock grotto she had discovered. She sealed the entrance with large rocks to keep out marauding animals. Their meager stores of flour, salt, and beans were now cached inside the cabin, hung from a lodge pole.

Angelique carefully catalogued their meager hoard. Maybe, just maybe, they would have enough.

That evening clouds swept in from the southwest. A storm churned the lake into mountainous waves with strong winds. Moisture that had been carried all the way from the Gulf of Mexico slid up over the cold arctic air coming down from the Polar Regions. As the Gulf air rose and cooled it wrung out the moisture that fell as rain into the cold air below. It froze. It coated rocks, trees and snow - everything - enclosing it in a prison of ice. The ice that had formed on the lake was broken up by the waves, tossed onto the shore, and formed a jagged wasteland of white. As the process continued the pressure ridges extended far out into the lake.

Inside the cabin, under wool blankets and a bearskin robe, Charlie and Angelique lay, dry and warm, contemplating an uncertain future.

The Lawyer

The tavern was on a side street on the south end of town, a neighborhood place where everyone seemed to know everyone else. Don entered and stood by the door, looking around the room. In the far corner a group was gathered, talking and laughing among themselves. Don approached, examining each face until . . .

"Eric? Eric Hoffman?"

A man about thirty, dark hair and eyes, well built, going slightly to paunch, turned toward the greeter, a tankard of ale in his hand. They looked at one another.

"Don? Don Engstrom? What in hell are you doing in Boston?" He threw his free arm around Don's shoulder. "Terry! Terry! A mug for my friend."

The bartender looked, smiled, and nodded as he drew a glass of beer.

"Geez, Don, how long has it been? Eight years? What are you doing here? Here, John, Bill,

Matt, this is an old school chum, Don Engstrom. Don meet the gang. What are you doing here anyway? I thought you went west to seek your fortune among the savages, mining - what was it? Copper, wasn't it?"

Nods, handshakes, friendly smiles 'round the group greeted him.

"West, yes, a fortune, no. Copper is the game. The mining is why I looked you up." The two took seats at the next table.

"How'd you find me?"

The barmaid slid a mug of beer across the table and left.

"Hah! Yeah! Well, it wasn't easy. I remember you talking about practicing law here, in Boston. I asked around 'til someone directed me to your office. Someone else sent me to your lodging. Your landlady sent me to this place."

"Well, I'm glad you found me. It's good to see you. I suspect there's more to this visit than 'How're you doing'."

"You see right through me, huh?"

"That's what we legal types do. See right through to the nitty gritty."

"Well, Eric, this has to do with nitty gritty all right. I think I need some legal help and I need it badly."

Don related the hiring of the Bodines and the refusal of the investment group to honor the arrangement. Eric interrupted with an occasional question, growing more serious as the tale unfolded.

"A copper investment group, Boston Bank and Trust, you say?"

"Yes."

"Smithers and Smithers are their attorneys. They're a big outfit in town. Was there a lawyer there?"

"Yes. Brown eyes, brown hair, five foot eight, maybe 165 pounds. Neat dresser."

"Yeah, that would be Ashbrook Smithers, a senior partner."

"So? Can you help me?"

"What do you want to do?"

Don looked up in surprise. "What do I want to do?"

Eric grinned at him and shrugged. "Yes, what do you want to happen? You tell me what you want to accomplish and I'll try to figure a way to do it. That's how it works."

"I don't have much money."

"We'll talk about the money later. You tell me what you want to do and we'll see what we have to work with. From what you've told me though, it doesn't look good."

Madness

The snow had nearly buried the cabin. Charlie

had made a pair of snowshoes intending to continue with a trap line through the winter. The trapping had gone well into January. Now, as the snow deepened and the temperature dropped, the daily trek became every two days, then three then it was abandoned entirely.

Angelique continued smoking and drying the meat, carefully managing their meager food supply. Meat was now the most plentiful commodity. Potatoes, roots, berries and the small amount of flour, coffee, and salt were fast disappearing. She carefully rationed the cranberries, feeding them once every seven to ten days, to prevent the black gum disease.

Charlie was more and more frequently lapsing into periods of preoccupation, talking to himself. He wandered back and forth in the small cabin like a trapped animal. The lack of windows created a dark and gloomy atmosphere. Outside the wind howled and tore at the cabin corner then raced away across the silent snow.

Both Charlie and Angelique were steadily losing weight. The darkness and the lack of exercise were depressing. Angelique was concerned about Charlie. He began wandering outside. He would flounder in the snow, in daylight or dark, raging, cursing at no one and nothing. He would shake his fists and shout threats of violence. He would rail against the three white men who had abandoned them on this dark and evil island. He began whetting his knife. Whenever he sat down he would take the knife from the sheath at his side and stroke it back and forth on a piece of stone. Angelique would wake in the night to hear the knife scraping back and forth, back and forth, back and forth in the quiet darkness.

She tried to divert his attention, to calm him, to talk with him, reason with him but it was all to no avail. The wild look remained in his eyes and he seemed not to hear. He began swinging his fists at her, striking her once when she attempted to get him to return to the cabin. She became concerned for her own safety. She was afraid to sleep day or night.

Charlie continued whetting his knife, sharpening it, testing its edge with his finger as he babbled incoherently. His eyes flitted wildly around the room.

Angelique began to steal things, a robe, some food, and was able to slip outside with them. She hid these things in a cavity in the snow at the base of a pine tree. It wasn't far from the cabin. The snow wouldn't allow her to travel very far. The pine branches had drooped under the weight of the snow. More snow covered the drooping branches leaving a hollow around the trunk of the tree. She broke off the lower branches to make a small room. She used the pine boughs as matting, as insulation from the cold ground.

When she would return to the cabin she would find Charlie whetting his knife, back and forth, back and forth. He would look at her with a wild grin on his face. One night, when Charlie had fallen asleep, Angelique slipped out to sleep hidden in her pine-tree cave. She slept fitfully, wrapped in a bearskin robe, fearing Charlie would find her.

Eating became a thing done in snatches as she continuously watched Charlie. Charlie did not eat. He began hallucinating, crying out that he saw a fine fat pig while he brandished his knife. He was looking at Angelique.

When Charlie next fell asleep Angelique crept close enough to steal the knife. She hid it in her cave.

Charlie spent the next few days alternating his raging and cursing with searching, over and over, in the same places, searching for his knife. He would fall into a stupor-like sleep more frequently, sleep for a period of thirty minutes - maybe an hour - and begin the cycle again.

Angelique discovered that if she remained still he seemed not to notice her. It was necessary to tend the fire, to add fuel. This always created a tense situation. She tried to time her movements with Charlie's periods of inactivity.

As the days passed Charlie seemed to be growing weaker. So did Angelique.

The Return

The anticipation of the coming spring was blotted out by the concern over his relationship with the Boston investors. They had not rejected his agreement with Charlie Bodine but neither had they endorsed it.

Eric Hoffman had listened to his explanation, questioned him about several details, and made suggestions. He said they would need depositions, sworn statements, and the documentation of people who had firsthand knowledge of the facts. It all sounded right and proper in the context that was Boston but out in the bush it just didn't fit. People who could neither read nor write had to do business on their word or a handshake. There wasn't anything else. These eastern lawyers just didn't seem to understand that.

The wooden sailing vessel groaned and creaked as she heeled over before the fresh wind. It was still cold and Don shivered under his heavy coat. Spray from the blunt bow slapping the waves arced high in the air. It paused briefly against the wind and then slid back to wet his face where he stood against the rail. Wiping the cold water from his face he retreated to the shelter of the deckhouse. Depositions! Sworn statements! He just didn't think it was going to work.

Shaking his head he dismissed these worrisome thoughts. By morning they'd be sailing up river to Detroit. That brought a smile to his lips. He looked forward to joining Redge, getting back to mining. That was something he understood.

The morning dawned bright and clear. When Don crawled out of his bunk in the forward hold and came on deck, there was land in sight on both sides. He found a cup of coffee and stood with the helmsman. The boat jarred slightly, regularly, as it moved forward through the waves.

"Yeah," the helmsman nodded, "we've had a fair breeze. We should be tied up before noon. Where you headed? Detroit?"

"Yes, for the moment. I'm meeting a fella' here and we'll be heading further north."

"Us, too. Got a little cargo to unload in Detroit then we're heading for the Soo."

Don let the conversation drop. He didn't want to reveal details of the mining operation - at least 'til he had talked to Redge. He wandered to the railing cupping his coffee close in his hand against the chill air. The feel of spring was in the air. The snow was disappearing with patches of bare ground showing through in the sunny spots. Buildings of Detroit were visible in the distance.

Don headed for the hotel as soon as the gangplank had been secured. Redge was registered but wasn't in. He was told that Redge was working for a local supply store.

When Don found Redge he was supervising a warehouse crew receiving, storing, and shipping goods.

"Redge! What are you doing here?"

"Gotta eat." He reached out to shake the offered hand.

"Eat? What are you talking about?"

Redge pulled out his watch, snapped the lid, and checked the time. "Don, I gotta finish up with this shipment. That over there," he indicated a corner of the warehouse, "is our stuff. You head back to the hotel. I'll meet you there in a couple hours."

"But, Redge, what are you doing working for this outfit?"

Redge chuckled. "At the hotel. It's a story I don't really understand myself. Maybe you can figure it out."

"Yeah, but . . ."

"Later, Don - - No! That doesn't go with this. Leave it." He turned back, grinning. Back at the hotel, we'll talk then. OK?"

Don stood looking at the other man, totally amazed at this turn of events. "OK."

Returning to the ship he had come on he discovered the boat would be held in port for two days. The supplies Don had acquired in Buffalo would continue to the Soo, consigned to Brian Hogue, when the ship left.

Back at the hotel he settled into a room and waited for Redge to return. He was anxious to know what Redge had stored for shipment north, how near they were to leaving themselves, and why Redge was working for the shipping company.

When Redge had returned and cleaned up the two went to the dining room to eat and talk.

As they sat and ordered a pre-meal drink, Don turned to his friend, cigar in hand, and said, "Well?"

Redge shook his head, shrugged his shoulders. "In order to arrange for the supplies we needed I had to make some sort of payment. Some of these folks wanted full payment before they'd order or hold anything."

"So? I can understand that. Why didn't you just pay them?"

Redge raised his hand defensively. "Who's telling this story, you or me?"

Don raised his hands, nodding his head. "OK. I'm listening."

"After you left I went to the bank to deposit what I had brought down with me. I only had $800."

"What? There should have been two - three times that much."

"There wasn't."

"Well, what happened? Where . . ."

Redge had raised his hand, stopping him. "I sent a message with one of the ship Captains asking Brian for some more money. I never got an answer. I did learn, through that Captain, that Brian was pretty busy on his own buying and selling supplies and furs up at the Soo. I don't know but it would seem he may have had a use for that cash - other than copper mining."

"And you didn't even have enough to live on?"

"I guess I would have had I known that was all I had."

"Damn! That son of a . . ."

"Wait now! Wait 'til we find out - 'til we know what's really happening."

"Yeah! You're right! I never did like that guy though. OK! So where are we now? How ready are we to head north?"

"Well, when I took this job I told them what the situation was, that I . . ."

"You didn't tell them," Don paused, glanced around, and lowered his voice. "You didn't say . . ."

Redge grinned at him, shaking his head. "That I had a job up north as soon as the spring break up. They agreed to hire me anyway. I do feel I ought to give them some sort of notice - so they can find someone before I leave.

Don nodded. "I agree, I agree. Beyond that, what?"

Redge chuckled and took a sip of his drink. "A few dollars to pay for the equipment I've got stacked in the warehouse."

"How many 'few dollars' is that?"

"Nine hundred sixty three dollars and seventy two cents at the last count."

"You got a list? What all is there?"

Redge pulled folded sheets of paper from his shirt pocket and laid them on the table. "There it is. Everything we agreed on - except for the men. We'll have to round up a crew. I've talked to a few guys already. One of them works for me at the warehouse, a Cornish fella', you know, a 'Cousin Jack.' He claims to know the mining business, 'says he's got a nose to follow a vein of ore. He's my foreman. He handles men well."

"So what are you sayin'?"

Cocking his head to one side, extending his hands, Redge shrugged. "So, he's our shift boss."

Don grinned and raised is glass. "To our shift boss!"

"Agreed then! Confusion to our enemies!"

"Yeah, and we've got a few."

"Oh?" Redge placed his empty glass carefully on the ring it had left on the table. He waved to the barmaid for two more drinks.

"Yeah." Don sighed. The big boys in Boston are ever so happy about the copper but they're giving me a hard time over the deal we made with Charlie.

"What's the matter with the deal we made with Charlie?"

Don, looking down, slowly shook his head. "Now that they've seen the copper samples, projected the profit, they feel Charlie gets too much."

"Damn! It was Charlie's gamble - and he won! He deserves it just as well as they do. Five shares! What are five shares to them?"

"I'm hoping I can count on you to tell them that." He looked up at Redge as the barmaid set the fresh drinks on the table, picked up the empty glasses, and walked away.

Redge picked up his drink, stared at the glass, then shifted his gaze to Don. "Whatever I can do."

"If we don't get it done . . ."

"Charlie is gonna cut our nuts off." Redge finished

"Amen." The two looked at each other. Don raised his drink, looked askance at Redge, and added, "and confusion to our enemies!"

"Amen!"

In three days a replacement for Redge was hired. Althorpe Penhale, the Cornish miner, agreed to "hire on," to supervise the mining crew they intended to hire. Penhale was a stocky man with sandy unruly hair, short of stature, and built like a barrel. His sparkling blue eyes were alert and full of fun. He asked if he might not be a part of the hiring. His Cornish brogue was so thick Don and Redge had trouble, at times, understanding him. And the crew of eight men he turned up with were as hard to understand as he was. They had hired a Cornish mining crew; wages 70 cents a day and board - a dollar a day for Al.

Arrangements were made with two ships heading north to carry the supplies and the men. One ship could have carried them all but they were able to expedite their move two days by splitting the men and equipment between the two boats. The ships cast off and headed north together.

Arriving at Sault Ste. Marie Don Engstrom immediately sought to find Brian Hogue. Redge stayed at the dock to arrange for the unloading and transport of the men and equipment to the Lake Superior shore.

There were only two Inns in town and Don had no trouble finding Hogue. He was seated in the bar reading a two-month old newspaper. He looked up in surprise at the sudden appearance of Don Engstrom.

"Well, hello! I wasn't expecting to see you so soon. Is Redge with you?"

Don shook the proffered hand and replied, "Redge is down at the dock seeing to the unloading of men and supplies. We've got a crew and we're ready to go as soon as the ice breaks. What do you hear of conditions on the lake?"

"There has been no movement so far that I've heard of. Some of the locals seem to think it'll happen any day now. Here, here, have a seat. Would you like a drink? It's a little early in the afternoon but - well - who cares."

"No, no thanks," Don replied as he took the

seat. "I guess we'll set up a camp with the crew up on the north shore. I'm anxious to head out as soon as possible. Charlie and Angelique are probably ready for some company."

Brian cocked an eye toward his companion before he replied. "I have some equipment that Redge sent up stored in a shed. I guess you could move that too."

"Yes, we'll take care of that if you'll show us where it is. How about you? Are you ready for the trip north?"

"Well, Don, there's been a little change of plans. I'll be turning the balance of the mining account over to you and heading east to Boston."

"To Boston?"

"Why, yes, yes. A few things have come up that require my presence. I've got some business to attend to back there this spring."

"I heard you were attending to some business here, too, last fall."

"Well, yes, that's right. I don't believe that has any bearing on our business here though." He watched his companion closely for a reaction.

"Redge had to find work too - in Detroit. He ran out of money. He had bought supplies on deposit expecting funds from you."

Brian did not respond.

"Redge says he asked for money to buy supplies but you didn't send it."

"I didn't hear anything about that. If I had I would have sent something. You can see there's seventeen hundred dollars and change in the account."

"So you won't be coming with us?"

"No! I'll be going to Boston on the first available ship."

"Something else, Brian. Back in Boston they said you didn't approve of the arrangement we made with Charlie Bodine."

Brian Hogue squirmed slightly under this interrogation. He consciously leaned back in his chair, looking down at his hands. Looking up suddenly he met Don's gaze. "That's correct. I didn't approve of giving that French Canadian guide and his Indian wife a share in the operation. That was too generous."

Don did not reply but continued to look steadily into the other man's eyes. Hogue finally looked away.

"Well," Don broke the silence, "show me the equipment you've got stored here. We'll arrange to pick it up then go transfer the money account. When that's done you can be on your way."

They rose, leaving the drinks, and headed for the door. The bartender called their attention to the unpaid bill. Hogue openly showed irritation at the incident and responded rather brusquely as he paid the tab. Don waited passively watching the other's embarrassment.

The transfer of the account took place with a

minimum of discussion. The banker looked closely from one to the other but made no comment. It was only a short walk to the storehouse but the hour was late and it was beginning to get dark.

"Let's leave this 'til tomorrow. It's too late tonight to be able to look it over, to sort it out."

Hogue nodded his assent.

"I'll pick you up at the hotel in the morning, say, nine o'clock or so. It'll be light by then."

Hogue nodded again and, without further word, turned and walked back toward his hotel.

Don turned the opposite way and headed for the encampment Redge was to set up near the beach. As he approached he looked over the bay in the fading light. There was ice, jumbled and stacked, as far as the eye could see. It appeared their departure to Minong would be delayed.

Alone

Charlie was reduced to raging weakly in his delirium. He lay wrapped in the moose hide. He didn't recognize Angelique and refused her attempts to feed him.

She no longer lived in the cabin. She would come by three or four times a day to try to look after Charlie. She realized there was little she could do but try to make him comfortable. She could only watch and wait.

Her makeshift cave under the pine tree had begun to deteriorate, melt and collapse. She had transferred her few belongings to the stone cave that had been the food cache. It had assumed the status of a permanent home. The small area was snug, protected from wind and weather. With a floor cover of pine boughs she slept there, retreating to her cave whenever she felt threatened or sleepy. With Charlie as weak as he was she felt she could build a fire in her cave.

When Charlie died Angelique was in the cabin, watching. She took the robe and left Charlie where he lay. She wouldn't have had the strength to do anything else even had she wanted to. She took the cooking implements, the axe, flint, and utensils and left the cabin. She would not return.

Angelique had no idea of time. The sun was moving north once again. Days were getting longer. The snow was beginning to melt though it froze again in the night. The icy grip of winter was loosening. Angelique was rationing her remaining food very severely. She had returned to the cabin once to scavenge food but Charlie's body, staring sightlessly in the darkness, had frightened her so badly that she would not again return.

One day she saw rabbit tracks. She had no weapon. She methodically plucked hair from her head, long black hairs, and wove them into a stout cord. She contrived a snare and placed it in a narrow passage along the trail. She plucked more hair and wove it into a fish line. She shaped a sharp splinter and fashioned a "gorge" type hook tying the short stick in the middle, baiting it in a manner that held it smooth with her line. When a fish swallowed it, hopefully, it would open crosswise and jam in the fish's throat.

She attempted to cut a hole in the ice with the axe but was too weak to accomplish it. Her clothing hung loosely on her frame of skin and bones. The supply of cranberries had long since been exhausted and her gums were turning black.

Winter's grip was slowly relaxing as the sun mounted higher and higher in the southern sky. Angelique, concerned only with day-to-day existence, did not notice.

Angelique slumped against a rock face in the warmth of the sunshine. The raw rabbit she had partially consumed was causing her severe abdominal pain. She rocked slightly, softly crooning. She did not know if she would live or die and, beyond a feeble spark for survival, was not concerned. She wondered if she should return to the cabin. She wasn't sure she would be able to. The spur afforded her when she saw the snare sapling jerking had sapped whatever reserves she might have had. Something was caught! Something to eat! She had torn at it with her bare hands, stripping back a bit of skin and sunk her teeth into the raw flesh.

A loud noise accompanied a flash of pain. Maybe this was the end. Maybe she would - another loud noise. It was a gunshot. It had come from the cabin. Charlie was -? No! Charlie was dead. Who? Could someone have come? Had someone found the camp?

She tried to rise, to run to the cabin, but only succeeded in losing her balance, tumbling from the rock to lie on her side. She attempted to shout but a course croak was all that emerged.

Back at the cabin Don Engstrom and Reginald Smith were among the first to arrive ashore. The place looked abandoned. Redge suggested they fire the gun a couple times, let Charlie and Angelique know someone had arrived. If they were very far away it might take them a while to return.

Redge headed back to where the men were unloading one of the boats.

"Hold up on that stuff. We're going to have to take it down to the site. We'll bring the boats around the point and down along behind the island here."

"Redge! Redge! Redge!"

He turned from the men and the boats, listening. "Yeah! Whaddya want?"

"Redge! Come here!"

He walked toward the cabin, concerned. That sounded like - must have been - Don. Was he over in the woods? Somewhere behind the cabin? Rounding the corner he saw him squatting beside a rock.

"Redge!"

"Yeah! I'm coming."

As Redge approached Don spoke. "I found Angelique here, beside this rock. She's nothing but skin and bones. She looks like she's about had it."

Redge, approaching, asked, "Is she dead?"

"Darn near. Gimme a hand. Let's get her back down by the cabin."

What's this?" Redge picked up a bit of fur and raw meat.

Don glanced at it. "I don't know. Gimme a hand."

They gently picked up Angelique, one on either side. She did not respond.

"Geezus! There sure isn't much to her."

Don nodded. "There sure isn't. I wonder what happened?"

"I'd say they were starving."

"They? Did you see Charlie? Where is he? How's he look?"

"No, no, I haven't seen hide nor hair of Charlie. Maybe he left her here. Is the canoe around?"

"Yes," Don replied. It's over behind the cabin."

"Well, then, where in hell is Charlie?'

"We'll have to ask Angelique when she comes around."

"If she comes around. She doesn't look good."

"First thing, make her comfortable, warm.

Then we'll get some hot soup into her. She could do with a wash-up too but that's another problem, one we can overlook for now."

"Let's not put her in the cabin. It smells like something died in there - a long time ago. Let's put her out here in the warm - -."

They suddenly stopped, looked at one another.

"Do you think . . .?"

"Charlie! Geeezus!"

"Let's just take her right aboard the ship. I'll come back and check."

Return Home

Passage was slow as the large ship painfully tacked back and forth against the westerly wind. The final run down toward the islands to anchor off LaPointe was executed swiftly and smartly. By the time the anchor was released several boats from shore were already crowding beside the hull. In one of them, a canoe, sat an aged Indian. A young brave sat in the rear, paddle in hand, patiently holding their position, waiting.

Don and Redge carried Angelique out of the ship's cabin on a pallet. As soon as she appeared the old man motioned with his hand. The young Indian reacted immediately. The canoe shot forward through the milling bateaus cutting off a larger boat and bringing a shouted curse from its occupant. As they drew alongside the old man grasped one of the trailing lines holding the canoe in position. Extended his free hand toward Angelique, he spoke to her in the Ojibwa tongue, "Come, my daughter. We have been waiting."

There was a sudden silence among those who heard. They looked in amazement from the two Indians to Angelique and back. Those crowding around in the smaller boats sensed the sudden change of attitude and paused. All grew quiet.

Angelique attempted to rise. The young Indian was at her side immediately. He picked up her wasted frame, carried her to the sideboard, and gently lowered her into the canoe. When she was comfortable he knelt in the rear and plied his paddle, backing water. As they moved the others cleared a way to the open water. The young brave then reversed his stroke, and the canoe sped quickly toward shore.

So surprising was this action that everyone stood as if paralyzed.

"Did you see . . .?"

"How in hell did that old guy . . .?"

". . . like he knew."

Don and Redge watched in amazement with the others. Dropping the empty pallet they gathered a few of their belongings and climbed into one of the boats.

"Say! Lad!" The Captain shouted from the

stern.

Don turned, waving his hand.

"Don't be long. I'd like to be able to ride this wind offshore before nightfall."

Don nodded, waving again in reply. Turning to Redge he said, "You head over to the trading post, arrange for anything Angelique might need. Give them a deposit if they want it. I'll catch up with that old Indian and make sure she'll be taken care of, tell them about the arrangement at the trading post. I'll meet you back at the dock quick as I can. We don't want the skipper leaving without us."

The old Indian was shuffling slowly down the trail when Don caught up with him. The young brave carried Angelique in his arms.

"We want to help. What can we do?" The old man met his gaze with steady dark eyes, slowly shaking his head.

The young Indian spoke. "He not understand. We," indicating the two of them, "care for sister."

Don explained that anything they might need from the trading post would be available - that the payment was already arranged.

A brief conversation in their native tongue brought a shake of the old mans head and a brief reply. "We not need white man medicine."

"Well - - anything you might need. Blankets. Food. Anything. It'll be there."

"Umph."

He watched them move slowly to the tepee. The Old Man held the flap as she was carried inside. He followed. The flap fell over the opening and all was still.

Surprised at the rebuff and uncertain if he should try again he stood perplexed. The distant ringing of the ship's bell broke his thoughts and he ran back along the trail toward the water.

Arriving at the shore he waved toward the ship hoping the Captain would see him. Redge was not back yet.

After a short wait he debated going to the ship alone, sending someone to hurry Redge along while he pacified the Captain. As he was about to initiate this plan Redge came running up.

"Did you get it done? Whatever they need is arranged for?"

Redge nodded breathlessly gasping, "It's taken care of." Shaking his head he continued, "No deposit. Ol' John says he'll trust us."

"Quick! Let's get to the boat! That old sea dog out there may leave without us."

On arriving at Minong the Captain was able to ease his ship between two of the islands and down the rocky chain with the help of lines and men ashore. He moored her near the digging site. The men they had left were hard at work breaking up the large pure copper chunks and digging up more. The emphasis was to load the ship, send out some copper as quickly as possible. They would delay erecting all but the basic housing needs and concentrate on shipping copper. When the ship was loaded they would divide the work force to improve their quarters for the summer. They would, however, continue to mine copper.

Don and Redge elected to alternate riding the freighter to the Soo. Once the connections with southbound shipping and the efficient transfer of ore around the St. Mary's rapids was established these trips would no longer be necessary. Their estimation of times, labor, tonnage of copper were unexpectedly accurate. A round trip with the ship allowed time enough for the men working on site to have another load ready by the time the ship returned. At times, as wind and weather dictated, they were able to build up a small stockpile that gradually grew. Below the Soo three additional ships were kept busy transporting the copper ore to a smelter.

With the operation running smoothly Don planned a trip to an investor's meeting in Boston. Redge would remain at Minong to supervise the operation.

Don rode one of their ore carriers as an informal inspector of operations south of the Soo. At Detroit he posted a message to Boston advising them of his estimated arrival there and continued on the freighter to Albany, NY. He spent two days at the smelter observing the percentage return of copper compared to ore delivered. Since a high percentage of the ore was float (nearly pure) copper the return was extremely high. The Boston investors should be highly pleased with their return.

Arriving in Boston two days ahead of schedule he immediately contacted Harold McNeil - Jerome Smithson, senior investor of the Copper consortium. He also discovered that he had arrived the same day as his posted letter.

A meeting of the board of directors was hastily called.

In the initial address Don apologized for his haste. He pointed out the shortness of the shipping season on the great lakes, the need to maintain a high rate of production, and his desire to return as soon as possible. He reviewed present and projected production, the richness of the ore, the return at the smelter, and cold hard dollars of gross profit. The presentation was warmly received.

The question again arose, introduced by the newly elected Corporate Treasurer, Brian Hogue, concerning the share in the corporation that had been promised the Bodines. The share return would exceed the estimated salary figure by a multiple of 23.4. The matter was tabled for possible discussion some time in the future – or not.

The Treatment

Evenings were still cold. A warm fire flickered in the center of the teepee sending shadows leaping and dancing on the walls. The ancient eyes of the old man glowed, reflecting the fire, two bright points of light in a wise and somber face. A pot of thick soup sat close beside the fire where it would stay hot. To one side, beneath a bearskin robe, Angelique had lain for the time it took the moon to wane and fill again. Whenever she stirred, moaned, or called in a delirium the old man was there. He fed her from the pot, gave her water, cleaned her and washed her.

Young Indians from the village came to the teepee every day to replenish the wood supply. He would give them instructions, send them for herbs and teach them to find what he needed. The young people always listened attentively for he was a very wise man. They always treated him with great respect.

Angelique's fever had raged for days during which time she ate nothing, drank only that which the old man pressed upon her. Her emaciated body, ravaged by starvation, was weakened further. Slowly the fever subsided. A thin soup, prepared from the herbs and plants the old man had requested, was gradually added to her water ration. She began to eat, to gain weight. The delirium subsided. She rested more easily.

No one knew of these changes in Angelique's condition. The old man was the only one who entered the teepee. His status in the tribe was such that no one inquired. Whatever he asked was done without question.

One clear day when the sun was high and the early spring flowers blanketed the forest floor the old man helped Angelique out of the teepee. She rested against a tree trunk in the warm sunshine. The annual renewal of life was all round her. As she soaked in the warmth and quietly watched the life in the forest around her, she gently held close in her hand a small, worn bearskin medicine bundle.

and so it goes

In later years Angelique took a position as a domestic in the household of an Iron Mining Magnate in the port town of Marquette. She was well suited to their needs as she was quiet, kept to herself, and demanded very little beyond her personal needs.

Donald Engstrom and Reginald Smith worked long enough to produce sufficient Copper to pay a generous return to their investors then moved on. Together they traveled southwest in search of greater challenges, larger ore deposits, bigger and better mining opportunities.

In the city of Boston in a rather fashionable downtown section are the offices of B. Hogue and Son, Inc., Accountants. Although they were newcomers to the established Boston accounting firms their aggressive and imaginative accounting practices had garnered them several lucrative accounts. In addition to accounting clients were advised on investments in which their accounting company participated. They planned to soon expand to larger offices.

The proprietor, B. Hogue, is widely known as one of Boston's prominent citizens, is an elder in the church, and is known as a local philanthropist. He resides in a 27-room mansion on a hill in the city's fashionable upper northeast side.

Visitors to the Lake Superior Island, now named Isle Royale, often search for the grave of one Charles Bodine. It was said he was an early pioneer who had found great wealth, gold, but had died on the island during the severe winter of 1844-45. No one has ever been able to find the grave or any gold. The wooden marker said to mark the site has never been found either. The tale remains another of the many mysteries and Charlie Bodine one of the many ghosts that are a part of the shadowy island the Indians called Minong.

♎

Photo courtesy Houghton County Historical Society

Cora and Fred Jeffers exemplify truly dedicated teachers. Fred turned down an offer to be superintendent of the Detroit Schools. He and Cora chose to remain with the land and people they loved.

Cora and Fred Jeffers

EDUCATORS

"Never in the field of human endeavor has so much been owed by so many to so few." I'm sure Mr.

Winston Churchill would not mind my paraphrasing his now famous pronouncement.

Education has seldom been an occupation that attracted individuals through the lure of financial reward. At higher levels there may be a few more dollars, prestige and academic honor that befalls a chosen few. Down in the trenches it's the dedicated educators, the foot soldiers that carry forward the battle for the development of the minds of children. Here are the true believers, those dedicated heroes and heroines who believe that a mind is a terrible thing to waste.

Early teachers were often single ladies – being single was a requirement – who worked for low wages. Females were expected, in those days, to accept lower pay than their male counter parts. Part of the arrangement very often was that they were boarded in the homes of families in the area in which they taught. Quite often the individual homes in which they boarded were also the schoolhouse. They taught all "grades" in the same class divided into groups as they saw fit.

Family economic conditions required many school children to miss schooling to assist at home, during harvest season for example. Large families were the social security system of the day. It was a cyclical thing. Large farms or more income were required to support large families – which demanded larger farms or more income.

Winter months were those times when the children's labors were not so much in demand. Indoor plumbing, as we know it today was non-existent to the working class. Children were often sewn into their winter underwear that they would continue to wear 'til spring. Putting it as gently as possible, a student group could become pretty "ripe" before the snow was gone.

There were standards to be met to advance in the various grades. The uncertainty of student's availability and sometimes-weak parental support toward education could result in a student becoming a young adult. In these situations these young adults were capable of undermining the teacher's ability to maintain discipline and decorum and disrupting the classes. Such was the case in Atlantic Mine School, a Copper Mining community near Houghton, in 1891 when Mr. James J. Jeffries was hired to teach.

Some of the schoolchildren in the Atlantic Mine School were in their late teens. They had intimidated previous teachers to the point where several had resigned.

Unknown to his new students Mr. Fred Jeffers had been orphaned at the age of five. He was a child who had been shipped west on an "Orphan Train." and was familiar with a rough and tough life.

Orphan trains were an attempt in the 1870s to resettle orphaned or abandoned children from populated areas in the east with families in the expanding west. Unfortunately many children were "adopted" and used as near-slave labor.

Fred was "claimed" at a train stop in Jackson, Michigan. He left a six year old brother still on the train and a younger sister back in Boston. It would be eighteen years before they saw one another again.

Fred was fortunate in that he was subsequently able to attend and graduate from High School and was able to work his way through a college in Ypsilanti, Michigan. He was offered the opportunity to teach in Atlantic Mine. He accepted. It wasn't until later in 1893 that he would marry a college classmate, Ms. Cora Doolittle, who would also come to the Keweenaw and teach. The two of them went on to establish an enviable record of having taught and been superintendent of the Adams Township Schools (which included Atlantic Mine) for a period of 55 years. Fred was elected to and served on the Michigan State Board of Education.

Mrs. Jeffers (Cora) was active in her own right. She was active in advancing the cause for women's suffrage. Joined by her husband she spoke at rallies across the Upper Peninsula often hiring halls at her own expense. When a need arose to conduct swimming classes she accepted the challenge and, in addition to her other duties, taught both boys and girls swimming. Some of those boys, returning as veterans of World War II in the Pacific Theatre, attributed Mrs.

Jeffers swimming classes to the saving of their lives during that conflict.

This is an educator's greatest reward; the recognition and appreciation of a student for the effort expended on their behalf. This is a real teacher's true reward. To see the mind, body and character that they have helped develop grow into something "greater than themselves."

I'll bet you thought I was going to ignore those problems Mr. Jeffers encountered back in 1891. You remember? The teenage students who intimidated their teachers? Here's a fact not known to those students. Mr. Jeffers had done some boxing back in college. In fact, with the name Jeffers, and a gentleman named James "Jim" Jeffries being the World's Heavyweight Boxing Champion at the time, Fred Jeffers had picked up the nickname "Jim."

When an older student attempted to physically intimidate him, the new teacher promptly knocked the challenger onto his backside. The boy retreated, went home and later returned with his father. When "Jim" offered to oblige the father in the same manner as he had the son the matter was settled without further confrontation. The two men became friends after this rather unusual introduction.

Fred and Cora (Doolittle) Jeffers. You're not apt to find their names in history books or prominently displayed on a bronze plaque somewhere. The hearts and minds wherein their care and concern achieved a special place are fast disappearing from the scene. Wherever it is that the permanent records are kept of those who have achieved greatness in the service of their fellow man, there you will find the names of Cora and Fred Jeffers.

The Keweenaw

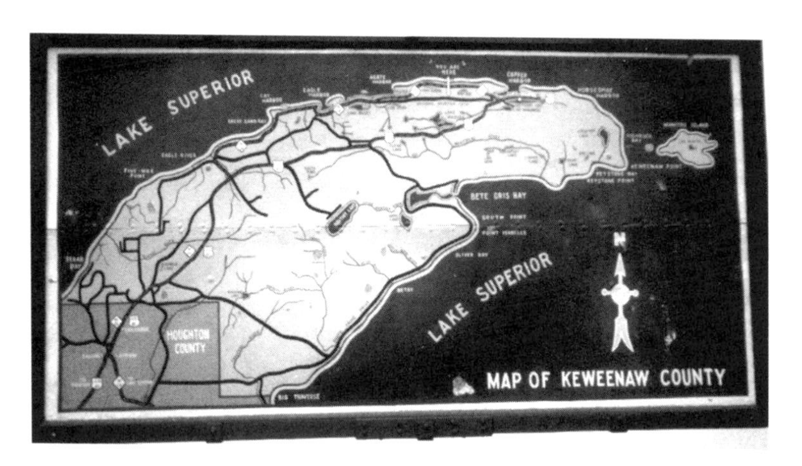

Keweenaw Peninsula

Jutting out into Lake Superior the copper discovered in this peninsula made millionaires of many Eastern investors

Discovery

The Keweenaw Peninsula is a huge finger of land (rock, some say) that juts out into Lake Superior some 65 miles from the Upper Peninsula of the State of Michigan. It was created – who knows how long ago - by the internal melting and meshing of molten rock as the earth was forming. Later it cooled and was chiseled and shaped by huge glaciers of ice a mile or more deep, glaciers grinding their way south from the Arctic. When this irresistible force met the immoveable rock the basins that became the Great Lakes were dug. The striations, the scars left by the meeting of these forces are still visible on the rock outcrops that are everywhere in this northern land.

Human habitation came about much later, after the forming and shaping of the land and the introduction of seedlings and animals and growing things. The land then lay awaiting human discovery of the resources that had been created

Explorers, archeologists, through the use of radiocarbon dating, have identified what they believe is evidence of the primitive mining of copper that happened about 1,400 B.C., some 3,400 years ago. The evidence of this mining activity was discovered on an island Native Americans called "Minong." With the coming of the French *Voyageurs* the island, located some 50 miles northwest of the tip of the Keweenaw Peninsula, was named Isle Royale. The area was sparsely populated at that time with Native Americans followed a pattern of subsistence, utilizing what nature provided.

The initial exploration by white men coming from the east was preceded by the influx of eastern Native American tribes forced from their homeland. The early interaction between the natives and the explorers involved the fur trade. The white man traded pots and pans, tools and blankets, firearms and whiskey in exchange for furs from the Indians. The

Indians became dependent on this exchange that slowly supplanted their subsistence way of life.

Missionaries accompanied the fur traders and explorers and, of course, set out to convert the natives from their tribal ways to Christianity. There was competition between the dispensers of the seemingly pleasurable effects of whiskey in the here and now with the formless promises of a better life in the hereafter.

In 1776 a large mass of copper that came to be called the "Ontonogan Boulder," was discovered upstream from the mouth of the Ontonogan River. It was thought to be 95% pure copper. With this discovery a group of British nobles petitioned the king for a grant of all mineral rights on Lake Superior. Further limited exploration underlined the complications of this remote location and discouraged them from further interest.

In 1822 Henry Schoolcraft headed an expedition to the area. Douglass Houghton, employed to make notes on the geography, minerals, soil condition and natural history of the area, accompanied him. During their exploration they found that much copper existed in the area in natural masses. The sites of this "float" copper were difficult to discover. Discovery had been made however and interest in development soon followed

The natives had no concept of land ownership in the white man's sense of the word. They were convinced to enter into several treaties by which "title" to the land was conveyed to the United States Government. In the 1840s a self-taught surveyor, William A. Burt, was hired to survey the peninsula. With ownership established and legal description available the way was open for serious seekers of copper.

At first the government leased mining sites agreeing to receive a portion of the mineral revenue as payment. This system was quickly abandoned in favor of outright sale at a price of $1.25 per acre. Financial interests in the east were quick to invest. Development of mining operations began in the area of Copper Harbor and Eagle Harbor.

Upon establishment of a claim labor had to be brought into the area. These men had to be provided with housing, they had to be fed, paid, and supplied with the necessities of life. All of this was done at a minimum cost in order to maximize profits. Labor was another of the items necessary to do business and was treated like the rest - to be procured with the least amount of trouble and at the lowest possible price.

The Copper Miners

Superior View Studios photo, Marquette, MI

Quincy Mine

This copper mine, known as "Old Faithful" for continuous dividends, has a shaft extending over 9,000 feet deep.

The Mines

The first copper bonanza was the Cliff Mine that, in 1849, produced 900 tons of 65% pure copper. Dividends paid to Cliffs stockholders between 1848 and 1870 would total $2,627,000. The price of a share of stock in 1857 had climbed to $175. By 1858 it was $300 and growing. The population near the mine on Eagle River grew from 100 people in 1852 to 300 people by 1862. The miners worked 8-hour shifts and received $15 to $20 per month.

It's interesting to note that a man named Justin H. Rathbone formed a fraternal group at Eagle Harbor in 1859. It was named the "Knights of Pythias." Its name derived from the story of two Roman Citizens, Damon and Pythias, who lived in the fourth century B.C. Pythias, convicted of some political intrigue, was sentenced to death. He begged to be given leave to travel to his home to arrange his personal affairs prior to his death. This was granted upon condition that his friend, Damon, take his place to die should Pythias not return. Pythias, although delayed along the way, did manage to return prior to the execution. Roman authorities, impressed by this display of faith and loyalty between these friends, released them both. This story motivated Justin Rathbone to form this group that gained official recognition in Washington, DC, in 1864 and had grown to almost a million members by 1921.

Between 1850 and 1860 Ontonogan with its docks, warehouses, four sawmills and several copper mines employing 1,419 people was the largest most prosperous town on Lake Superior. In 1848 Samuel O. Knapp discovered the Minesota Lode near Ontonogan. Stockholders invested $366,000. By

1867 the Minesota mine had paid them $1,760,000 in dividends. In 1846 the Quincy Mine was established and in 1850 discovery was made of the Pewabic amygdaloid lode that would ultimately reward investors handsomely.

With the 1860s came the civil war with its demand for copper – and men. With much of the work force taken for military duty and the market demanding copper the search for men to work the mines took on new significance. Miners were paid an average of $41.50 per month and were working ten-hour shifts.

Management of the mines varied from greed to concern for the workers and views that were in between. Samuel S. Robinson, a former schoolteacher from back east, followed editor Horace Greeley's widely published admonition to "go west, young man." He learned the mining business on the job. He credited his success to careful attention to details and interests of his employers while maintaining a "religious regard" for the rights, health and comfort for the men under his control.

In 1862 Houghton was called the most important village in the Upper Peninsula with a population of 2,000.

The creation of the St. Mary's ship canal – the locks at the Soo – in 1855 had eliminated a major obstacle to the shipment of copper.

Mining companies cooperated to raise money to send recruiters to Norway and Sweden to recruit immigrants to fill the need for labor. Many of the immigrants never made it to the Keweenaw having been hired at a bounty of $300 to serve in the Union Army. Miner's wages had risen to $65.45 by 1864.

With this influx of immigrants, most of whom could speak no English, came management problems. Crews were naturally made up of like nationalities that spoke the same language. They further gathered in social groups where they observed their own customs and traditions. "Outsiders" were looked upon with suspicion. A strike by the underground miners occurred in 1861 wherein the men demanded higher wages. Management was adamant in denying the demand believing that any concessions would encourage demands and strikes in the future. After a week the miners returned to work. Greater immigration was encouraged by management through influence in Washington to "flood the woods" with labor before capital could be held hostage to labor's demands.

Consolidation of several independent mines, including the Quincy Mine, in 1871 created the Calumet and Hecla Mining Company. Alexander Agassiz assumed the Presidency of Calumet and Hecla, "C&H," and thus began a flourishing period at the mines under the control of what could be called a benevolent dictator.

In 1865 stock in Calumet and Hecla was held at $1.00 per share. Many discouraged investors sold out at that price, a move they would come to regret. Within seven years it had paid its (mostly Eastern) stockholders $8,000,000 dollars in dividends and would continue rewarding them handsomely. By 1899 a share of Calumet and Hecla stock was selling for $189. It was said, during this period, that the four most famous names in the New England states were Lexington, Concord and Calumet and Hecla.

♎

The Copper Miners

Superior View Studios photo, Marquette, MI

Calumet

Housing for the miner's families in the village of Calumet about the turn of twentieth century.

The People

Among the immigrants the Cornish, coming from a mining area of Cornwall in Britain, seemed to have a natural aptitude for mining. They almost naturally became the job foremen and mining captains. It was also said, with bitterness among other nationalities, that when a particularly desirable job was available, the captain always had a "cousin" who was also available, hence the term "Cousin Jacks" when referring to the Cornish. The Cornish also brought with them the somewhat socialistic English relationship between labor and management and were very instrumental in getting company supported medical care and accident insurance benefits.

It was the Cornish who introduced the now famous "pasty," a meat and vegetable pie completely enclosed by a pastry shell. This allowed a miner to carry his lunch wrapped and inside his shirt where it could be kept warm until it was time to eat.

Slowly the racial, religious and ethnic barriers were eroded. The kids played together and although expressions like "dirty finn" and "wop" and "dumb polack" might be shouted at one another it was without the vehemence with which they might have heard it. Girls and boys met and were attracted to one another in spite of the suspicions of their elders. The great melting pot that was and is a magnificent feature of the United States of America was working.

Ownership of a piece of farmland seemed to be a dream of every Finnish immigrant and was attained by many. Many Irish left the mines to own and operate a bar. Jewish residents started businesses many of which exist yet today. And who hasn't had pizza in an Italian restaurant? There were African Americans who lived and worked in the Keweenaw area even before the Emancipation Proclamation. In 1860 Rebecca Gleeves, a 25-year-old black woman who had been born in Virginia operated a hotel in Eagle River.

The conditions under which the working class lived and raised their children was probably unimaginable to people today – even those of us who are presently living below the poverty level.

There was no "welfare" back then. Large families were the social security people planned for in their old age. Numerous children, in addition to being dependent on their parents for their care and feeding, were also contributors. On a farm they could and did contribute through the chores that were assigned to them. The work ethic was taught early.

Living conditions and sanitary facilities were a personal matter unencumbered by any laws or codes. There was no such thing as a bathroom. To allow for the waste from normal human bodily functioning there was a little house back away from the main house called the outhouse. It was nothing more than a hole in the ground over which a shelter was built for privacy and, in winter, some protection from the elements. A seat was built over the hole and, for those more fortunate, a Sears or Montgomery ward catalogue sufficed for a roll of "Charmin." To provide for the call-of-nature that might occur during the night a large jar or pot was kept usually underneath the bed. It had to be dumped, of course, in the morning. Many were the size of a three or four gallon pail with a slightly flared top and a lid – and what a noise that lid would make in the still of the night.

Facilities for bathing were the nearest creek or stock pond. When the weather turned too cold for outdoor bathing the only recourse was a laundry tub beside the kitchen wood stove. And the water had to carried from the nearest creek or cranked up in a bucket from an outside well. The more fortunate might have a hand pump and some of them were outside too. Once the water had been hauled in it had to be heated in a bucket on the wood stove. If you were fortunate you would be one of those to use the water first. Families were large. And privacy? I'll let your imagination answer that. This was not a joke or a weekend outing. This was everyday life. You might understand why bathing was not something that was done regularly even in the summer time. There was even a school of thought that held that too frequent bathing would weaken a person. Then too there were lumberjacks who believed that by avoiding bathing, becoming "stinky" enough would keep the bugs away from them.

Scandinavians might cooperate in building a community bathhouse, called by the Finns a "Sauna." This was a relatively small two room building with a stove surrounded by rocks and a stadium-like tier system of seats almost up to the ceiling. The second room might contain a bench and a large open water tank and pegs to hang clothing. It was here that bathers would remove their clothing on the way in and rinse off and dress on the way out.

A "sauna" was a bit of a production and might only be done on weekends. Men would build a hot fire in the sauna stove in advance to heat the building and the rocks surrounding the stove. They would also have to fill a tank with water. A schedule was arranged with a time for the ladies to bathe and a separate time for the men and boys.

The idea was to sit, naked on the benches and allow the heat to generate perspiration, to sweat. Flailing oneself lightly with aspen or cedar boughs often augmented the process. Water sprinkled on the hot rocks generated steam that induced even greater perspiration. After a period of time in this superheated steambath a person would leave for the changing room to rinse off and get dressed.

At times the heat was almost too much to allow a person to breathe. I can remember "taking sauna" when some of the older men would have it so hot in there that I had to lay on the floor to find air cool enough to breathe – and they would be sitting on the topmost bench pointing and laughing at me.

In winter it was not uncommon for mothers to sew children into their winter underwear. It wouldn't be taken off or changed ‘til spring. From midwinter ‘til spring downwind of these kids is not where a person would wish to stand.

The situation regarding laundry was much the same as bathing. The woman of the house – with help from older daughters – had to haul the water, heat it on the wood stove and fill the washtub. Naptha soap, a kind of deep yellow bar, would be “shaved,” much like whittling wood, into the tub and mixed with the water. Clothing would then be scrubbed against a corrugated washboard to clean it. Each garment would them be wrung out by hand, rinsed in another tub of water, and wrung out once more. Those in a higher income bracket might afford a hand-operated wringer, two rubber rollers held tight together, through which the clothing would be fed while someone turned the crank to rotate the rollers. After all this the washed clothing would be hung on a clothesline outside to dry. In late fall and winter it would often freeze stiff as boards. Then it had to be hung indoors wherever room could be found. Walking through the house could often be like feeling your way through a jungle.

Getting up on a winter morning was often a series of moves not looked forward to. First leaving the warm bed to answer the call of nature – while shivering. There was no insulation for the homes back then and the “central heating system” was mom getting up earlier and stoking up the fire in the kitchen stove. After unavoidably rattling the lid on that under-the-bed pot – also called a "Thunder Mug" – there was a scooping up of clothing and a mad dash for the kitchen and the warmth of that stove. I could go on but this is enough to give insight to personal hygiene and the "rules of the boudoir."

As communities grew and expanded greater communication with the outside world developed. It was said that the copper mines in Montana paid higher wages. This was countered with the argument that living conditions and fringe benefits were better here. C&H President Agassiz' benevolent management had provided a library for the community along with a company hospital and accident insurance for the miners. In 1900 the famous Calumet Theatre opened with a seating capacity of 1,200. The elegant Hotel Scott opened in Hancock in 1906. There was even a rumor that the Michigan State Legislature had failed by one vote to make Calumet the Capital of the State.

Education was another great social leveler of ethnic differences. By 1910 88 to 95 percent of the boys and girls between the ages of six and fourteen were attending school. Many older immigrants also attended night school to learn to read, write, and understand the English language. As people came to know one another, to develop common interests – and a common language – they began to realize that they had much in common as a people and as miners.

♎

The Copper Miners

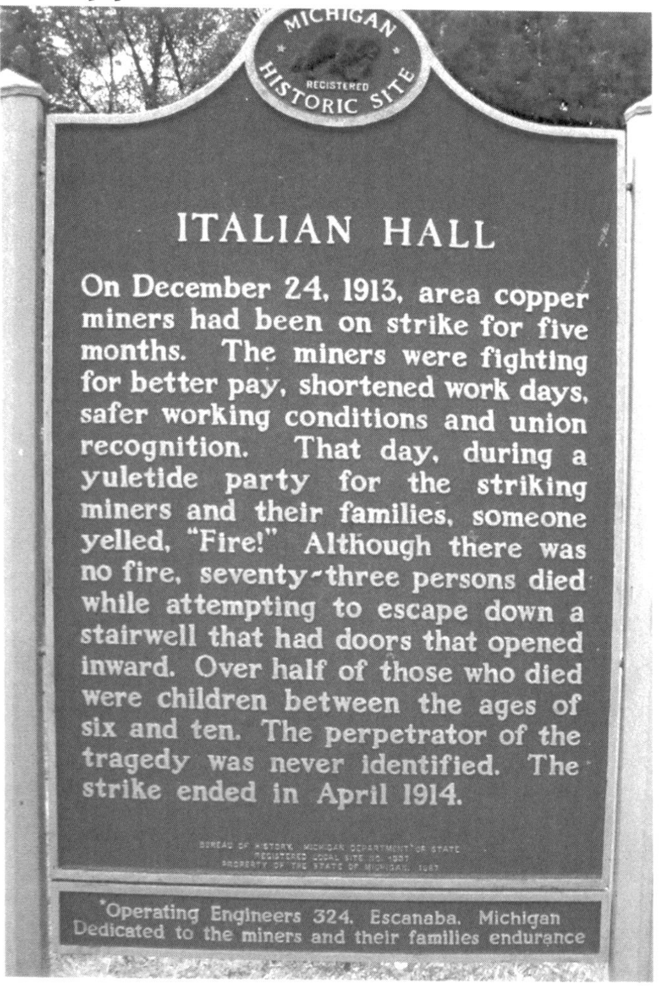

Italian Hall Memorial

Commemorating the disaster of Christmas Eve, 1913.

The Italian Hall Disaster

In the early 1900s labor groups were attempting to organize workers. Labor throughout the country was coming to believe that the only way they could bargain with employers was by exhibiting a common front. This would introduce a new term into labor management relations. It would be called "collective bargaining."

To malign these labor groups management labeled them "Socialists" or "Communists" – and some were. One group was called the "International Workers of the World," the "IWW," also called "The Wobblies." Another was the "Western Federation of Miners," the "WFM." The WFM was destined to play a tragic part in the Keweenaw Copper industry.

In 1913 long simmering grievances between labor and management broke out in a strike. The WFM was encouraging the workers to strike. Some agreed. Some didn't. The ensuing strike would involve the Michigan National Guard, pit neighbor against neighbor and generate senseless acts of violence on both sides. And, in the end, no one would have won. A tragedy occurred which overshadowed the strike. It generated accusations and recrimination on both sides and brought profound grief to the entire area. It came to be called the Italian Hall Disaster.

During the strike some relief assistance was forthcoming from the WFM and other union groups.

The Women's Auxiliary of the Western Federation of Miners arranged to hold a Christmas party on the twenty fourth of December. It was to be held on the second floor of the Italian Hall in Calumet. There would be gifts for the children and a respite for the adults from the hard times brought on by the strike.

During the height of the festivities someone yelled, "fire!" Panic filled the room. Some few called out, "No! No! There is no fire" but the damage had been done. What followed was a mad rush of people to the single stairway and the double doors at the foot of the stairs. There was one thought in the mind of the crowd. "Get out!" The first ones to arrive at the doors attempted to open them but the crowd was too close behind them. They couldn't open the doors. The doors opened inward and with the crush of the crowd stampeding down the stairs there was no chance.

Seventy-three persons died in the crush of bodies and the trampling of feet on those stairs. Over half of the victims were children. No one ever knew who it was who shouted "fire" in that crowded hall. No one that is except that person himself.

The strike ended on April 12, 1914. No one's goals had been achieved. The company had not condescended to the miner's demands. The company had passed up a chance to engage in collective bargaining and would have to confront the challenge at a future date.

What happened? What went wrong? Accusations and explanations flowed freely. Success has a thousand fathers but failure is an orphan. Just like the identity of the culprit who yelled fire in the Italian Hall that evening no one would ever really know. It would be another thirty years before the copper miners would once more challenge management. The second time, more successfully organized, they would finally achieved collective bargaining rights.

♎

The Copper Miners

Once a Miner's Home

This miner's house, near the Deleware Mine in Keweenaw, followed the fortunes of copper mining.

The End of Copper

The price of copper experienced a slump shortly after that. World War I created a temporary surge in demand but the 1920s once more saw a depression in the prices due to worldwide over speculation. Copper mining faced poor long-term prospects. With Henry Ford offering $5 per day on his automobile assembly lines many people left the area for the factories of Detroit. Competition from Chile and central Africa further depressed the market. The Keweenaw mineshafts were deep underground. The Quincy shaft, the "Old Reliable" of the copper industry, had reached a depth of 9,070 feet.

In October of 1939 C&H announced that its last deep shaft had been permanently closed. Seventy-three years and 3.275 billion pounds of copper had been mined but the end had come. C&H would continue to operate a couple of small operations in Keweenaw County for another thirty years but the end had come. Another confrontation between labor and management occurred on April 3, 1969. That was the end. Calumet and Hecla ceased. The era of copper in the Keweenaw was over.

Those who stayed on in the Keweenaw found other occupations. Agriculture provided an income for some. Others found work in the woods cutting and hauling pulpwood for the burgeoning paper industry. The University at Houghton was expanding but the area was a ghost of its former self. As a part of President Roosevelt's relief programs of the 1930s several projects were initiated for the area. A new dock was built at Eagle Harbor. An eighteen-hole golf course was constructed near Brockway Mountain. Several stone monuments, stone boats sailing out of the side of hills were built. They didn't really represent anything but they provided work. It all helped. But the people of Keweenaw were survivors. They hung on.

In later years former residents who had left for better opportunities, had reached retirement age. Many of those retirees returned. Their roots were still deep in the red dust of Keweenaw, the copper country.

Tourism had always been a feature of the area. The clean air and beautiful surroundings appealed to asthma sufferers and travelers seeking peace and solitude. Through the efforts of local citizens the Keweenaw has now been designated a National Historic site. Federal assistance has been obtained and the area has been set aside as the Keweenaw National Historical Park.

Tourism will never equal the fortunes made from the bowels of the peninsula. It doesn't matter. The people who live here never saw any of those fortunes. They didn't come here looking for material wealth. They came looking for the good life – and the good life is still here.

♎

Bay Cliff's Children

Children from the Bay Cliff Health Camp participate in the Big Bay Independence Day Parade. Among other things, more "Independence" is what the health camp encourages for these children.

WHERE DREAMS COME TRUE

In a small village in Northern Michigan is the Bay Cliff Health Camp. Bay Cliff was once the 165-acre estate that, in the 1920s, had been a timber baron's residence and also housed a dairy farm. When logging operations terminated the dairy farm was not capable of supporting itself. The dairy herd, cattle that had been imported from England, had been put up as collateral for a loan. With the demise of the dairy farm the local banker quite unexpectedly became owner of the dairy herd.

The house and grounds were not included in the collateral package and were passed to the lumber baron's sister and brother in law. That couple decided to continue operating as a farm but not for dairy cattle. They experimented with breeding chickens, raising dogs, rabbits, goats, and mules. There are many humorous stories about their animals wandering loose about the Big Bay area but we'll have to save that for another time. Suffice it to say they too were unsuccessful. Then came the Bay Cliff Health Camp.

In 1930 Goldie Corneliuson, a public health physician with the Michigan State Health Department, and Elba Morse, a nurse and superintendent of the Northern Michigan Children's Clinic, met while both were employed by the Children's Fund of Michigan. This took place during the great depression of that time. These two health care workers were seeing first-hand the effects of the hard times particularly on the children. Hunger and want stalked the land. The two women often discussed the health problems they were encountering, particularly the consequences on those least able to care for themselves, the children.

They were in agreement that something had to be done. They were encountering too many malnourished children whose bodies were paying the price. Nourishing meals could prevent and correct many of these needless physical disorders. Proper food, rest, sleep and recreation in a worry free environment could correct many of the problems. The children needed a place where they would be free to enjoy recreational activities with others of their own age with full bellies. They needed to be able to sleep in warm beds.

With their decision made to correct this injustice these two ladies forged ahead and never looked back. Funding for the project came from wherever they could beg, steal or borrow. Arrangements were made to purchase the 165-acre estate in Big Bay, then called Chedna Farms.

What had been cow barns became dormitories. The chicken coops became medical centers. The house became an office and dining facility. They would reclaim the estate's former title and named it The Bay Cliff Health Camp.

The children in the first group would be limited to those between the ages of three to 18. They would be from the Upper Peninsula of Michigan and must be recommended by their various county health departments and nurses.

The Bay Cliff staff had to be screened and was composed of doctors, nurses, college students (as counselors), therapists, cooks and almost anyone else who would donate their services for darn little compensation. This was to be "for the kids." That statement of Bay Cliff's mission would never change.

The intent for the children of the Bay Cliff experience was to clothe, feed, treat ailments, provide recreation and to love them. The emphasis would be on full bellies, security and lots of love.

The first group arrived in 1934. The staff began caring for, feeding and loving them. The medical staff straightened clubfeet, repaired teeth and taught the basics of good health and hygiene. Counselors provided companionship, support and security. Each child had someone they could turn to whatever their question or problem. In addition to the immediate beneficial efforts to improve the quality of their lives it was hoped these children would later carry the health care lessons home with them to their parents, their siblings and friends.

Although all didn't always go smoothly there was no stopping an idea whose time had come – particularly when advanced by two courageous and determined women like "Doctor Goldie" and "Aunt Elba."

Henry Ford, the automobile manufacturer from Detroit, would often visit Bay Cliff when he was in the area. One witness to such a visit was firmly convinced that Mr. Ford would never return again. Aunt Elba purposefully steered him to a child suffering from a correctible medical condition. He was told that this condition could be corrected but the child's parents could not afford the treatment. I guess this next would be called "a pregnant pause." In 1915 Henry Ford had financed and built a hospital in Detroit. That hospital was still operating, a fact of which Nurse Morse was very familiar. Mr. Ford suggested that the child be sent to Detroit to receive treatment, at Mr. Ford's expense of course.

"And, of course," Aunt Elba remarked, "the parents would have to accompany the child and would need somewhere to stay."

"Of course," replied Mr. Ford. And they did as beneficiaries of the generosity of Mr. Henry Ford.

Did Mr. Ford ever return to Bay Cliff? "Of course" and regularly.

Since its opening Bay Cliff has been a nonprofit, nondenominational, nonsegregation facility with but a single purpose: what is good for the children.

Over the years caring for the children has expanded. Today it includes handicapped children, children who are deaf, who are blind, those with cerebral palsy and those with speech defects and reading difficulties. It would be easier to list those who can't attend – and I can't think of any.

The kids come in all shapes and sizes and various colors too. Many are repeaters having been "campers" at Bay Cliff before. For others it's their first time. The procedures are the same.

When they arrive the first "caregiver's" jolt is that all parents, relatives, etc. are sent back home. They're told, "Don't come back 'til the child's seven week experience is over." Some find that unacceptable. They feel their child needs special care and handling. They don't realize that these Bay Cliff children have never received better care in their lives. The approach is not "take care of" or the "don't let anything happen to" or "poor little . . . " This care is directed more toward the popular army-recruiting slogan; "Be All That You Can Be!"

Experience at Bay Cliff has found that many well-meaning parents are inclined to want to shield the child against failure: They are hesitant to encourage them to try to talk - or walk - or whatever their shortcoming might be. They fear the child may fail and feel crushed by the experience. The Bay Cliff approach is so what if you fail. Try something else. No great accomplishment was ever attained by someone who was afraid to fail.

Couple this "can-do" attitude with the support and love of the Bay Cliff Staff and of the children in similar circumstances and failure is no longer a specter to be feared. "Be all that you can be!" With encouragement and support it is truly miraculous what children are capable of accomplishing. It is no accident that the postscript to "Bay Cliff Health Camp" is "A place where dreams come true."

One little fella of my personal acquaintance was born handicapped and began his life in a wheel chair. He had pretty much been raised to accept that he would require care and had learned to sit quietly in his wheel chair. I guess he was eight years old when he came to Bay Cliff. He was shy, almost withdrawn. His folks couldn't afford it but a way was found. In the Bay Cliff environment he was loved and cared for but he was also encouraged to try new things, to "be all that he could be." When his parents came to pick him up they hardly recognized the boy. He was outgoing and extroverted and quickly made new friends. He wasn't walking and running but he had discovered he was capable of being very mobile without his wheelchair. "A place where dreams come true."

Everyone is included in camp activities. There is camping, swimming. Boating, even meals are a time for fun and games. When the kids gather for a choral serenade those children who are deaf will "sign" through the lyrics of the songs. No one is left out.

Adding to the accomplishments of the children it is notable that camp counselors, those young people who counsel and befriend the children, are mostly repeat "campers" themselves. They don't come back because the pay is good and there are no fringe benefits – well - not in the collective-bargaining sense. Fringe benefits accrue in another form. If you ask a counselor why they return year after year they almost act embarrassed to answer. They may look down, scuff a foot, and then they'll look back, almost defiantly – right in your eye – and they'll say, "It's the kids." Those kids often give more than they get.

Every Fourth-of-July there is an Independence Day Parade held in Big Bay. Even the name, "Independence Day," has special connotation to the campers at Bay Cliff.

The parade happens during the annual summer Health Camp period. Each of the children at Bay Cliff, individually but most often in groups, participate in that parade. Some walk, some are in wheel chairs, some ride in trailers or the back of a truck but all can participate. Spectators never fail to cheer and applaud and encourage them. There's amazement on the faces of the children when they realize that the applause, the attention, the cheering is for them.

As a spectator you may not get to see the whole parade. There's a tendency for a persons eyes to cloud up, maybe even rain a little, but it's worth it. You can't visit Bay Cliff without it affecting you, without being changed yourself.

No, you won't find the names Goldie Corneliuson or Elba Morse listed on any monuments even though Bay Cliff has served as a model for other health camps all over the world. They didn't achieve great financial wealth. They weren't prominent in politics. They turned their backs on those disciplines. They did change their corner of the world though and for the better. And they will never be forgotten in the hearts of the children they touched. We should all be so fortunate.

TO ORDER BOOKS

Additional copies of this or other of the author's books may be obtained through:

Still Waters Publishing
257 Lakewood Lane
Marquette, MI 49855-9508
(906) 249 9831
(866) 236 1972 (toll free)
bmukk@chartermi.net
www.benmukkala.com

Cost:

"Copper, Timber, Iron and Heart"	$15.95
Shipping & Handling	3.05
Total cost	$19.00

Other books by Ben Mukkala:

Touring Guide, Big Bay& Huron Mountains	$9.95
Come On Along, Tales & Trails of the North Woods	$14.95

plus a couple bucks for shipping.

Enjoy!

AUTHORS BIOGRAPHY

Ben Mukkala

is a native of Marquette, Michigan, a graduate of Gravaraet High School in Marquette and Ball State University in Indiana. He enlisted in the United States Air Force during the Korean War, rose through the ranks and served a tour in Southeast Asia flying F-4 "Phantom" jet powered fighter-bombers. He retired in 1970 with the rank of Major.

Subsequent to retirement, he flew various aircraft, sailed boats, and traveled extensively. He enjoys the outdoors and an active life. He began writing during his Air Force career and has been published in several flying and outdoor magazines and various newspapers. He has published several books.

He is the father of three daughters and one son, and stepfather to two sons and four daughters. He currently lives with his wife, Dorothy, in Marquette.

Ω

Front Cover Index

Lumberjacks at a meal in a lumber camp dining hall.

Present day iron ore truck used in open pit mining operations.

Modern Ore Carrier with self unloader visible above the deck inbound to Marquette MI for a load of iron ore pellets.

Towering white pine tree 17 feet in circumference, 6 feet in diameter.

Bay Cliff Children take part in Big Bay's July Fourth Parade.

Locks at Sault Ste. Marie, MI enabling boats and ships to be raised and or lowered past the St. Mary's River rapids.

Rear Cover Index

Display of early logging tools and equipment.	Face of the Jackson mine, first Iron Ore mine in Upper Michigan - 1880.
Anderson's fishing boat "Peter A."	Lake Superior and Isle Royal.
"Quincy" copper mine at Hancock, MI – early 1900s.	Marquette, MI lower harbor and pocket ore dock, circa 1890s.
The schooners "Moonlight" and "Kent" ashore on Chocolay Beach near Marquette MI - 1895.